The
Straw Ox

and other tales

BY

F A N   K I S S E N

Script Writer and Program Consultant
Elementary School Division
WNYE, Board of Education Station
New York City

HOUGHTON MIFFLIN COMPANY
The Riverside Press Cambridge

Contents

THINGS YOU WILL WANT TO KNOW 4

Rumpelstiltskin 8

Boots and His Brothers 22

The Three Wishes 34

Lenka's Little House 48

The Straw Ox 62

What the Good Man Does Is Right 74

Jack and the Beanstalk 88

Shiro and His Master 104

The Sleeping Beauty 116

The Rock in the Sea 128

The Peterkins Try to Become Wise 140

3

Things You Will Want to Know

Why are these stories called Tales from the Four Winds?

The four winds come from the north, south, east, and west. The stories in this book come from many different places too. They come from countries all over the world.

Most of these stories are old tales. No one knows who first told them, but for hundreds of years older people have been telling these stories to children. The children liked to hear their favorite stories told over and over again, just as you do.

Sometimes a story that comes from one country will remind you of one which grew up in another land. In Denmark they tell a story called *What the Good Man Does Is Right*. It is very much like *Hans in Luck*, a German tale.

Boots and His Brothers is a story told in many lands in different ways. It is the story of a youngest son who is laughed at, but who does a hard task and receives a great reward, sometimes marrying the princess.

We can see, then, that people all over the world are very much alike. They laugh at the same things, cry at the same things, like the same good things, and hate the same bad things.

What can you do with these stories?

You can read these tales silently by yourself, just as you would read any story, but you will enjoy them even more if you take part with others in reading them aloud.

One group in your class might use any one of these tales

as a make-believe radio program for the others in the class to listen to. The tales in this book were written as radio plays, and they have really been used on a radio station as a program for children.

Your class might have a make-believe radio program to which other classes in the school could be invited. You can even have a real radio program if there are loud-speakers in the classrooms in your school.

What might you do in a radio play?

When you take part in a radio play, you may have one of many different parts. You may have a great deal to say, you may have only a little to say, and you may not say a word.

You may be one of the *cast*. The cast is the name for all those who take the parts of the people in the story. When you take the part of a person in a radio play, you read everything that the person says. You try to read it just the way the person would say it.

You may be the *announcer*. The announcer tells the name of the play and something about the story. He also tells when the play is over. If you are giving the play for another class or for part of your own class, the announcer tells the names of those who took part. He reads all the parts that come after the word ANNOUNCER.

In each of these plays there is a part for the *narrator*. *Narrator* is just another word for story-teller. In a radio play, not all of the story is told by reading the things which the people in the story say. The narrator tells the parts of the story that are not read by the cast. He reads everything that comes after the word NARRATOR.

5

Perhaps you would like to be the *sound man*. When you listen to plays over the radio, you hear many different sounds. You may hear horses galloping or rain falling. Of course you know that there are not real horses galloping around the studio and that it isn't really raining. Those sounds are made by the sound man.

If you are the sound man, you must watch for the word SOUND in the play. You must be ready to make the sound that you are told to make there.

At the beginning of each play, you will find a list of the sounds which are needed. You will also find pictures which show you how to make the sounds.

Before the play begins, be sure that you have ready all the things you need to make those sounds. Some sounds, such as the moo of a cow, are made by the voice of one person. If there are many different sounds in one play, more than one sound man may be needed.

Every radio play needs someone to be in charge of the music. We might call him the *music man*. If you are the music man, you must have music ready for each place in the play where you see the word MUSIC. The music may be made by playing part of a record, or children may sing or hum part of a song that fits the story.

What do such words as (Bridge), (Laughs), and (Up) mean when they are printed in italics and are in parentheses?

Bridge: In a play on the stage, the curtain is closed between parts of a play. The audience can't see what is going on in a radio play, so music is played between the parts. This music is called a bridge. It carries you across from one part of the play to the next.

Up, Out, and Under: You will sometimes find the word

up, or *out*, or *under* after MUSIC and with the words which tell what sound is to be made.

The word *up* means that the sound or music should begin or should be made louder.

The word *out* means that the sound or music should stop.

The word *under* means that the sound or music should go on but should be very soft so that the person who is reading can be heard.

Sometimes you will find some words in parentheses ( ) before or among the words which you are to read. These words should not be read aloud.

Sometimes the words will tell you how to read what comes next, as (*Slowly*). Other times they will tell you something you should do, such as (*Laughs*) or (*Weeps*).

When you come to the word (*Fade*), it means that your voice should grow softer.

(*Fade in*) means that your voice should be soft at first and then grow louder.

(*Off mike*) means that your voice or the sound should sound as if it came from far away.

Now you know what these words mean, and you know what each person has to do in a radio play. You are ready to have your own radio plays and perhaps a make-believe radio station to broadcast the *Tales from the Four Winds*.

Rumpelstiltskin

CAST   MILLER   FIRST SOLDIER
            ELSA   SECOND SOLDIER
            KING   THIRD SOLDIER
            DWARF   ANNOUNCER
                  NARRATOR

SOUNDS

Key in lock

Door open and shut

Stamping of foot

8

ANNOUNCER: Hello, boys and girls! It's story time. You like to hear stories, don't you? In every country round the world children like to hear stories of fairies and witches, brave princes and beautiful princesses, clever tricks and silly tricks of people and animals. Listen, and we'll tell you a story that the children of Germany like to hear. The story is called *Rumpelstiltskin.*

MUSIC: (*Up and out*)

NARRATOR: Once upon a time there lived in Germany a poor miller who had a beautiful daughter. As she grew older he wondered how he was to find a good husband for her. (*Fade*) One day he said to his daughter,

MILLER: I am beginning to worry about you, Elsa, my child.

ELSA: Worry? Why, Father?

MILLER: It is time for you to marry, but I have no money to give to a husband.

ELSA: Then who will marry me, except a man as poor as we are?

MILLER: You have no money, it's true, but you are a very beautiful girl, beautiful enough to be a queen.

ELSA: (*Laughs*) A queen! Oh, Father!

9

MILLER: (*Thoughtful*) A queen! If only the King could see you!

ELSA: The King? How could I ever get in sight of the King?

MILLER: If he ever saw you, Elsa, I'm sure he would wish to make you his queen. Now, how can I make that happen? Ah! I think I have an idea!

ELSA: What is it, Father?

MILLER: I must tell it to the King first. Go on with your spinning while I think it out.

MUSIC: (*Bridge*)

NARRATOR: The next day the miller and his daughter went to the palace of the King. (*Fade*) A soldier stopped them at the gate.

FIRST SOLDIER: Halt! Who goes there?

MILLER: A miller, soldier. I live down by the river.

FIRST SOLDIER: And this girl?

MILLER: She is my daughter, my beautiful daughter, Elsa.

FIRST SOLDIER: And what would a miller and his daughter want with the King? Go around to the kitchen if you want to sell your flour.

MILLER: I must see the King himself. I want to do him a favor. Let me pass, please.

FIRST SOLDIER: (*Laugh*) You, a poor miller, want to do the King a favor?

MILLER: Yes. You see, my daughter can do something wonderful. She can spin straw into gold.

ELSA: Oh, Father!
What are you saying?

10

FIRST SOLDIER: Oho! That is something the King would really like to see. He's always needing gold. You may go into the throne room.

SOUND: (*Door open*)

FIRST SOLDIER: But you, girl, wait out here till the King sends for you — if he does.

ELSA: Father! Don't go!

MILLER: Thank you, soldier. (*Fade*) Wait here, Elsa.

SOUND: (*Door shut*)

KING: Well, who are you, man, and what do you want?

MILLER: Your Majesty, I have a very beautiful daughter.

KING: Is that all you have to say? There are many beautiful girls at my palace.

MILLER: My daughter is not only beautiful. She can do something wonderful. My daughter, your Majesty, can spin straw into gold.

KING: Well, that *is* something different. I always need gold, and more gold.

MILLER: Yes, your Majesty. If you will only see her.

KING: Straw into gold! Bring her here this afternoon.

MILLER: Your Majesty, my daughter is waiting outside this room.

KING: Ah! So much the better! Soldier, take the miller's daughter into one of the rooms. See that it is filled with straw, and have a spinning wheel put in, at once.

SECOND SOLDIER: At once, your Majesty.

MILLER: Wouldn't you like to watch my beautiful daughter as she spins, your Majesty? Just one look?

KING: No. Go, now, miller, and tell your daughter to start spinning at once. If she does not spin all the straw into gold by morning, she shall die.

MILLER: Oh! Your Majesty! But —

KING: Go, I said. Soldier, see that the girl is locked into the room all night. Go, now, both of you.

MUSIC: (*Bridge*)

NARRATOR: Then Elsa, the miller's daughter, was locked into the room full of straw. She was told to spin the straw into gold by morning or die. Poor Elsa didn't know what to do. (*Fade*) She started to cry.

ELSA: Oh, dear! What shall I do? What shall I do?

DWARF: (*Cross, gruff voice*) Good afternoon, miller's daughter.

ELSA: Oh! Where did you come from, little man?

DWARF: I came through the keyhole. Why are you crying, miller's daughter?

ELSA: The King has ordered me to spin all this straw into gold by morning. If I don't, I must die. Why, I don't even spin wool very well.

DWARF: What will you give me if I spin it into gold for you?

ELSA: Oh, could you spin it for me? I have no money, but I'll give you my velvet hair ribbon.

DWARF: All right! It's a bargain. Now
let me sit down at the spinning wheel.

MUSIC: (*Bridge*)

NARRATOR: The little man spun and spun quickly, until
all the straw was gone and all the spools were full of
gold. Then he was gone as quickly as he had come.
(*Fade*) Early the next morning the King came and
opened the door.

SOUND: (*Key in lock, door open*)

KING: Ah! Gold! So you really can turn straw into gold,
as your father said.

ELSA: You see the gold before you, your Majesty.

KING: Lovely, shining gold! Now, miller's daughter,
you shall be put into a larger room full of straw. Spin
that into gold before morning, if you love your life.

ELSA: But, your Majesty, —

KING: No "buts." Soldier, have a larger room filled with straw. Take the girl and her spinning wheel into it.

SOLDIER: It shall be done at once, your Majesty.

MUSIC: (*Bridge*)

NARRATOR: So Elsa was taken into a larger room which was filled with straw for her to change into gold. (*Fade*) She looked at the straw and began to weep.

DWARF: How do you do, miller's daughter?

ELSA: Oh! The little man again! I'm so glad to see you! Please, will you help me again to-day?

DWARF: Tell me first, what will you give me if I spin this straw into gold for you?

ELSA: I will give you the gold ring from my finger.

DWARF: Very well! Give me the ring. Now let me sit down at your spinning wheel.

MUSIC: (*Bridge*)

NARRATOR: The next day, when the King came to the room, he looked at the spools and spools of gold, and smiled with pleasure. This time he looked at the miller's daughter, too. He saw that she was beautiful, but he wanted still more gold. (*Fade*) He led her into an even larger room filled with straw.

KING: You must spin for me one night more, miller's daughter.

ELSA: But, your Majesty, I cannot.

KING: Why not? You have done it twice. Do you refuse to do it again?

ELSA: Oh, no, your Majesty, but —

KING: If it is all spun by sunrise, you shall become my queen.

ELSA: Oh, your Majesty! But how can I —

KING: How can you, a poor girl, marry a king? Why, you can spin more gold than any princess ever had. Not another word, now. Set to work.

SOUND: (*Door shut and locked*)

ELSA: (*Weeps*) Oh, dear! Oh, dear! If only that little man would come again!

DWARF: Here I am, miller's daughter.

ELSA: Oh! Thank heaven you've come again! Please, little man, will you spin for me this third time?

DWARF: What will you give me this time?

ELSA: Oh, dear me! I have nothing left to give you.

DWARF: There is one thing, and only one, for which I will spin to-night.

ELSA: What is that?

DWARF: Promise me that when you are Queen you will give me your first child.

ELSA: Who knows if I shall ever become Queen? Very well, little man, I promise that if I become Queen you shall have my first child.

DWARF: That's what I want! Now I'll sit down and spin.

MUSIC: (*Bridge*)

15

NARRATOR: Early the next morning the King came again, (*Fade*) and found the room full of spools of gold.

KING: Ah! More gold! How the room shines with its light!

ELSA: I am glad your Majesty is pleased.

KING: I am, and I shall keep my promise. You shall be my queen.

ELSA: Oh, your Majesty!

KING: Now that I look at you well, I see that you are really as beautiful as your father said.

ELSA: Thank you, your Majesty. I shall try to be a good queen.

KING: I shall order the ladies of the palace to dress you for our wedding.

MUSIC: (*Wedding march*)

NARRATOR: So the miller's daughter and the King were married, and they were very happy. About a year later the Queen had a beautiful little son. By this time she had forgotten all about the little man and her promise to him. (*Fade*) But one night, as she sat with her baby in her arms, the little man came into her room.

DWARF: Good evening, Queen.

ELSA: Oh! The little man who helped me spin the straw!

DWARF: Yes. Now you must keep your promise. Give me your child.

ELSA: Oh, no, no! I can't give him up! I can't!

DWARF: But you promised!

ELSA: Oh, I know I promised. But it was to save my life. Oh, please, kind little man! I'll give you anything else you say — gold, jewels, anything, but not my baby! I love him so!

17

DWARF: Nothing else will do. But I'll give you one chance to keep your baby.

ELSA: What is it? I'll do anything.

DWARF: I'll give you three days to find out my name. If you do that, you shall keep your child. If you don't guess my name, you must give him to me as you promised.

ELSA: Oh, thank you, little man, for this chance. I'll try to guess your name.

DWARF: (*Strange laugh*) You'll have to try very, very hard!

MUSIC: (*Bridge*)

NARRATOR: The Queen did not like to tell the King about the little man. She lay awake all night thinking of all the names she had ever heard. (*Fade*) The next night the little man came again to the Queen's room.

DWARF: (*Laugh*) Well, Queen, what do you think my name is?

ELSA: Is your name Henry?

DWARF: No.

ELSA: Is it John?

DWARF: No.

ELSA: (*Fading*) Is your name Joseph? George? Arthur? William? (*Dwarf laughs after each name.*)

DWARF: It isn't any name you have ever heard. My name is so strange that you'll never, never guess it. (*Scene ends with dwarf's laugh.*)

NARRATOR: The next day the Queen sent soldiers out to learn all the queer names that they could. (*Fade*) When night came, she cried as she waited for the dwarf.

DWARF: Well, Queen, do you think you know my name now?

ELSA: Is your name Shorty?

DWARF: No, it is not.

ELSA: Is your name Spindleshanks?

DWARF: No, it's not.

ELSA: Are you called Crosspatch?

DWARF: No, I'm not called any of these. You have one night left, Queen, to try to guess my name. If you don't guess it by to-morrow night, I shall have your child! (*Fade laugh*)

MUSIC: (*Bridge*)

NARRATOR: The Queen was very much worried that third day. Each soldier came back saying he had heard no new name. (*Fade*) But the last soldier told a strange story.

THIRD SOLDIER: Your Majesty, I saw a strange sight today.

ELSA: Will it help me guess the little man's name?

19

THIRD SOLDIER: Perhaps. I was coming through a dark forest. I came to a tiny house. I walked quietly over to the window and looked in. Hopping up and down before the fire was a strange little man. As he hopped he sang,

"To-day I brew, to-morrow I bake,
Next morning I the Queen's child take.
How glad I am she does not know
My name is Rumpelstiltskin!"

ELSA: That *must* be my little man! Thank you for your good news. Take this piece of gold as a reward.

THIRD SOLDIER: Thank you, your Majesty.

MUSIC: (*Bridge*)

NARRATOR: (*Fade*) Soon after the soldier had gone, the little man came into the Queen's room again.

20

DWARF: (*Laugh*) Well, Queen, this is your last chance. What do you think my name is?

ELSA: Are you called Conrad?

DWARF: No.

ELSA: Is your name James?

DWARF: No.

ELSA: Then your name must be — Rumpelstiltskin!

DWARF: (*Angry*) The fairies must have told you! The fairies must have told you! (*Snarl, foot stamped*)

ELSA: (*Laugh*) Now you can't take my darling baby! Stamp your foot as hard as you like! Ah! You've stamped your foot into the ground, and you'll never be able to pull it out again!

DWARF: (*Snarl and stamp of foot*) The fairies must have told you! Aaaah! Aaaah!

ELSA: Oh! Now your other foot is deep in the ground! Why, the little man is sinking down! He's gone! Now he'll never be able to harm my baby. (*Happy laugh*)

NARRATOR: Yes, the little man sank down into the ground and was never seen again. And the Queen kept her baby and was very happy.

MUSIC: (*Up and out.*)

ANNOUNCER: And so ends the first of our *Tales from the Four Winds*, the story called *Rumpelstiltskin*. I'm sure you were glad to know that the King married the miller's daughter. And weren't you happy when she guessed the strange little man's name and did not have to give him her baby?

Be sure to listen to our next story, called *Boots and His Brothers*. It comes from Norway.

Boots and

CAST   PETER   SOLDIER
           PAUL   KING
           BOOTS   ANNOUNCER
              NARRATOR

SOUNDS

Shovel digging

Water gurgling

Chopping of wood   Tree falling

Shovel against stone

His Brothers

ANNOUNCER: Hello, boys and girls! It's story time again. Today we will tell you a story that has been told for many years to the children of Norway. The story is called *Boots and His Brothers.*

MUSIC: (*Up and out*)

NARRATOR: Once upon a time there lived in Norway a farmer who had three sons, Peter, Paul, and John.

Now John, the youngest, was made to do all the dirty little jobs around the house and farm. He had to clean the barn and black the family boots, so he was called Boots.

One day the farmer told his sons that the farm was too poor to give them a good living, so they had better go out and seek their fortunes somewhere else. (*Fade*) The three brothers talked it over among themselves.

PAUL: Where do you think we should go, Peter? You're the oldest, so you should know best.

PETER: I don't know, Paul. I must think it over.

BOOTS: I'd like to see the big city. I wonder what it looks like.

PETER: That's Boots for you! Always wondering!

BOOTS: I wonder where the King's palace is.

PAUL: Everybody knows, silly, that the King's palace is on top of a high, high hill of hard rock.

PETER: That's why the King is in trouble, Boots.

BOOTS: What kind of trouble, Peter?

PETER: The hill is so rocky that nobody can dig down deep enough to make a well.

PAUL: And even if they could dig deep enough, the hill is so high that they couldn't get water up to fill the well.

PETER: Perhaps brother Boots doesn't know that you can't make water run uphill.

BOOTS: I wonder if there isn't another way of filling a well than by digging till you find water?

PAUL: There he goes, wondering again!

BOOTS: I think I'll go to the King's palace and see it for myself.

PETER: You can't see much of the King's palace.

BOOTS: Why not?

PETER: Because of the huge oak tree that grows by the palace wall. It's so big that the branches shut out all the light from the palace windows.

BOOTS: Then why doesn't the King have that oak tree cut down?

PETER: Because, silly, it's a magic tree.

BOOTS: I wonder what's magic about it.

PETER: You tell him, Paul!

PAUL: Well, every time one chip is chopped out of the tree, two chips grow back in its place.

BOOTS: Is that so! Maybe a good woodchopper hasn't tried.

PAUL: Listen to him! Don't you think the King can get the best woodchoppers in the country?

BOOTS: Why don't *we* try, you, and Peter, and I?

PETER: I never thought of that, Boots. It might be a way of making our fortunes. How about it, Paul? Suppose you and I try it.

BOOTS: And I, too.

PAUL: Well, all right, let's all go to the city together. You may come along if you like, Boots, just to watch us.

BOOTS: I'm coming, brothers. (*Fade*) I wonder if there isn't some other way —.

MUSIC: (*Bridge*)

NARRATOR: So the three brothers, Peter, Paul, and Boots, started out for the King's palace. By and by they heard a noise. It sounded like an axe chopping away at some wood.

SOUND: (*Axe on wood up and under*)

BOOTS: Listen, brothers! What's that noise?

PETER: I don't know, I'm sure.

BOOTS: I wonder what it is?

PAUL: There he goes, wondering again!

BOOTS: I'll go and see.

PETER: Go ahead, Boots, but don't expect us to follow.

BOOTS: Wait here for me. (*Fade*) I'll be right back, brothers.

NARRATOR: So Boots went off into the woods by himself. The sound of chopping grew louder and louder.

SOUND: (*Chopping up and under*)

NARRATOR: Soon Boots saw — what do you think? An axe, chopping away all by itself. Boots thought that might be a handy thing to have some day.

SOUND: (*Out on chopping*)

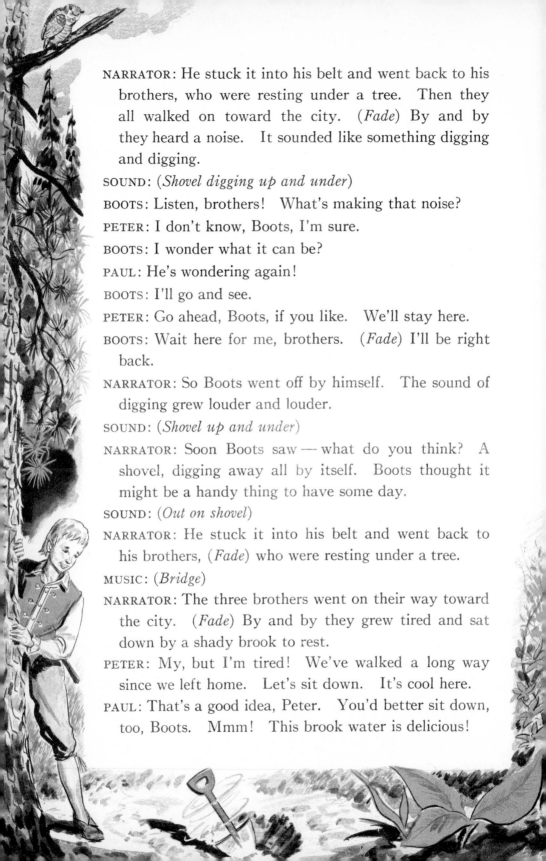

NARRATOR: He stuck it into his belt and went back to his brothers, who were resting under a tree. Then they all walked on toward the city. (*Fade*) By and by they heard a noise. It sounded like something digging and digging.

SOUND: (*Shovel digging up and under*)

BOOTS: Listen, brothers! What's making that noise?

PETER: I don't know, Boots, I'm sure.

BOOTS: I wonder what it can be?

PAUL: He's wondering again!

BOOTS: I'll go and see.

PETER: Go ahead, Boots, if you like. We'll stay here.

BOOTS: Wait here for me, brothers. (*Fade*) I'll be right back.

NARRATOR: So Boots went off by himself. The sound of digging grew louder and louder.

SOUND: (*Shovel up and under*)

NARRATOR: Soon Boots saw — what do you think? A shovel, digging away all by itself. Boots thought it might be a handy thing to have some day.

SOUND: (*Out on shovel*)

NARRATOR: He stuck it into his belt and went back to his brothers, (*Fade*) who were resting under a tree.

MUSIC: (*Bridge*)

NARRATOR: The three brothers went on their way toward the city. (*Fade*) By and by they grew tired and sat down by a shady brook to rest.

PETER: My, but I'm tired! We've walked a long way since we left home. Let's sit down. It's cool here.

PAUL: That's a good idea, Peter. You'd better sit down, too, Boots. Mmm! This brook water is delicious!

BOOTS: I wonder where this brook comes from?

PETER: There's Boots again! Always wondering!

BOOTS: I think I'll follow the brook up and see where it comes from.

PAUL: Go ahead, if you like. Peter and I have more sense than to go chasing brooks through the woods.

BOOTS: Wait here for me, brothers. (*Fade*) I'll be right back.

NARRATOR: Boots followed the brook. As he walked along its banks, it became smaller and smaller. Soon he found where the brook started. The water was coming out of — guess what! A brown walnut shell. Boots picked up the shell, stopped up the hole with some green moss, so that the water could not run out, and put the shell into his pocket. Then he went back to join his brothers.

MUSIC: (*Bridge*)

NARRATOR: After a while the three brothers reached the city. They walked up the high, high hill to the King's palace. Through the iron fence they could see the huge oak tree that spread its branches across the windows of the palace. (*Fade*) The soldier at the gate stopped the brothers.

SOLDIER: Halt! Who goes there?

PETER: We are three brothers from a far-away farm.

SOLDIER: What do you want here?

PETER: We want to try to chop down the oak tree.

PAUL: And we want to try to dig a well for the King, too, a well deep enough to hold water for a year.

SOLDIER: Ha! Ha! Ha! You make me laugh! So many men have tried and could not do these things! And what about you, young man? What's your name?

BOOTS: John is my name, though every one calls me Boots. I'm the youngest of us brothers.

SOLDIER: And do you, too, think you can cut down the tree and dig the well?

BOOTS: I'm just wondering if I can. I'd like to try, please.

SOLDIER: Come this way, the three of you. Oh! Oh! Here comes the King himself, with his soldiers, to look at his big tree. He does that every morning and every evening. Better stand at attention.

KING: Soldier, what are these three men doing here?

SOLDIER: They are three brothers, your Majesty. They say they would like to try to cut down the tree and to dig a well.

KING: Well, let them try. My dark palace is making me sadder, and angrier, too, every day. You, there! You look like the oldest. What's your name?

PETER: Peter, your Majesty.

KING: Take the axe from my servant and see if you can chop down this tree. But before you start — have you heard my latest order? Better tell him what it is, soldier.

SOLDIER: The King has ordered that whoever tries either to cut down the tree or to dig the well, and fails, shall be thrown into prison for a year. Whoever tries to do both, and fails, shall be put into prison for two years.

KING: Do you still want to try, Peter?

PETER: Yes, your Majesty. I am a good woodsman. Watch me.

SOUND: (*Axe on wood*)

KING: Harder! Chop harder, Peter!

PETER: (*Breathless*) I'm doing my best, your Majesty.

SOUND: (*Axe out*)

KING: It's no use. I can see the tree growing thicker wherever you cut one chip out. Oh, you make me so angry! Soldier, throw him into jail for one year!

SOLDIER: Perhaps, your Majesty, Peter would also like to try to dig a well. Then he could remain in prison for two years.

KING: Right, soldier. Keep him here. You, there! What's your name? You're next.

PAUL: I'm Paul, your Majesty. Let me have the axe.

SOUND: (*Axe on wood up and out*)

KING: You might as well stop, Paul. You're doing no better than Peter did. And what's your name, lad?

29

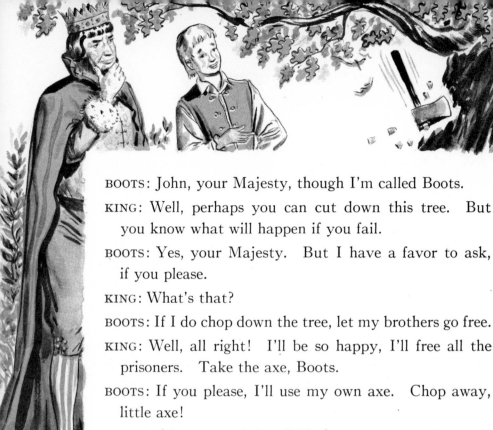

BOOTS: John, your Majesty, though I'm called Boots.

KING: Well, perhaps you can cut down this tree. But you know what will happen if you fail.

BOOTS: Yes, your Majesty. But I have a favor to ask, if you please.

KING: What's that?

BOOTS: If I do chop down the tree, let my brothers go free.

KING: Well, all right! I'll be so happy, I'll free all the prisoners. Take the axe, Boots.

BOOTS: If you please, I'll use my own axe. Chop away, little axe!

SOUND: (*Axe on wood, tree falling*)

KING: The tree is down at last! Peter and Paul, your brother Boots has freed you and all the other prisoners.

PETER AND PAUL: Thank you, your Majesty!

KING: Wait! Don't go yet. You must try to dig a well for me. You may have to go to prison for not doing that.

PETER: I'm sure I can dig the well, your Majesty.

KING: Go ahead, then, Peter. Right here. Take the shovel from that soldier.

SOUND: (*Shovel against stone*)

KING: I see you're getting nowhere, Peter. Stand aside and let Paul try.

SOUND: (*Shovel against stone*)

PAUL: I'm sorry, your Majesty. I can't break this rock, either.

KING: Stand aside, then, and let Boots try. Take the shovel, Boots.

PETER: Oh, your Majesty! Boots isn't strong enough!

PAUL: Your Majesty! Boots is too young and weak!

KING: Let him speak for himself. Boots, do you want to try to dig the well?

BOOTS: Yes, your Majesty. But you must promise you will not put my brothers into prison if I dig it.

KING: I promise. Now, take the shovel and dig.

BOOTS: If you please, your Majesty, I would rather use this shovel of mine. Dig away, little shovel!

SOUND: (*Shovel on rock up and under*)

KING: Stop, Boots! (*Out on shovel*) That hole is deep enough. I can't see the bottom. Thank you, Boots!

BOOTS: I'm glad I could do it for you, your Majesty. And my brothers are free?

KING: Your brothers are free. This is wonderful! But wait!

BOOTS: Yes, your Majesty?

KING: What good is a well without water? How am I to fill it? There's no water down there, and no one can get a brook to run up this high hill.

BOOTS: Oh, I can help you with that, your Majesty. I have a brook right here, in my pocket.

KING: A brook in your pocket! Nonsense! How can that be?

BOOTS: Look at this walnut shell, your Majesty. The brook is in here. If I take out this bit of moss, the water will flow out and keep on flowing forever.

KING: I'll have to see it to believe it, Boots. Go ahead. Drop the shell into the well.

BOOTS: I take this moss out, and — there! Flow, little brook!

SOUND: (*Water gurgling up and out*)

KING: The well is full! I have a well full of water at last! Where did you find this wonderful walnut shell, Boots?

BOOTS: In the woods, your Majesty. I saw a brook and wondered where it came from. I followed it, and there was this shell with the water flowing out of it.

PETER: That's the kind of lad this brother of ours is, your Majesty. Boots is always wondering about things.

KING: But he tries to find the answers. I wish I had more men like him to help me rule my kingdom. I have an idea! Boots!

BOOTS: Yes, your Majesty?

KING: How would you like to stay here in my palace?

BOOTS: Live in the royal palace?

KING: I will have my wise men teach you about the laws of the kingdom. And — yes! — you shall marry my daughter.

BOOTS: I, marry the Princess, your Majesty?

PETER: Our young brother, Boots, to marry the Princess!

KING: And when I am gone, you will be King in my place.

PETER AND PAUL: Boots a king!

KING: What do you say, Boots? Does that please you?

BOOTS: (*Slowly*) I wonder! It is a strange thing to happen to me, your Majesty, but I'm sure I shall like it.

KING: Come into the palace, then, Boots, and meet the Princess, who will be your wife.

MUSIC: (*Bridge*)

NARRATOR: So Boots, who was always wondering, married the Princess. He found places in the palace for his father and brothers, and so their fortunes were made.

MUSIC: (*Up and out*)

ANNOUNCER: And so, boys and girls, ends *Boots and His Brothers*, our story from Norway. Boots always wondered about things, but he always tried to find the answers. This time Boots was well paid for finding the answers to what he wanted to know.

Listen again next time when we'll tell you *The Three Wishes*, a tale that is told in Sweden.

33

The Three

CAST   PETER   FAIRY
            INGA   ANNOUNCER
            NARRATOR

SOUNDS

Fall of pack

Door open and shut

Chair moved

Light taps on door

Thump on table

Wishes

ANNOUNCER: Hello, boys and girls! Today our story comes from Sweden. It is called *The Three Wishes.* Do you think it would be fun if you could have anything you wished for? Are you sure? Don't be too sure until you have heard *The Three Wishes.*

MUSIC: (*Up and out*)

NARRATOR: Once upon a time there was a man who lived with his wife in a little hut at the edge of a forest in Sweden. He made his living by cutting wood and selling it in the nearby town. But that did not bring them much money, and they often had very little to eat.

One evening the woodcutter came home from the forest with a heavy bundle of sticks on his back. (*Fade*) He dropped his heavy load outside the door and went into the house.

SOUND: (*Fall of heavy pack, door open and shut*)

PETER: Hello, Inga. I'm home again.

INGA: What kept you so late, Peter? It's been dark for a long time.

PETER: I worked until nearly dark, and my bundle of sticks was so heavy that I couldn't walk very fast.

INGA: You work all day, but we have very little to show for it.

PETER: Well, the sticks I cut today ought to buy us enough food for a week.

INGA: I hope so, Peter. We have very little in the house tonight.

PETER: Well, as long as there's just a bite for my supper now, I'll be satisfied. What can you give me for supper, Inga?

INGA: All we have is a small loaf of bread, and some cheese, and a few potatoes baking in the fire.

PETER: Oh, that's not so bad, though I must say I'd rather have a nice roast chicken, or some lamb chops, or something like that.

INGA: Roast chicken! Lamb chops! How could we ever buy those?

PETER: Well, I didn't say I expected to get it. But wouldn't it be wonderful if a fairy just left it on the table for us some day?

INGA: A fairy! Huh! I don't believe in fairies. There aren't any.

PETER: I'm not so sure about them myself, Inga. But it would be fun to have a fairy fly in and say, "Hello, Peter! What would you like for supper?"

INGA: Stop talking nonsense, Peter, and start slicing this loaf of bread.

PETER: I'm glad our table stands at the window, where I can watch the stars.

INGA: Better watch that knife instead of the stars, or you'll be cutting your fingers.

PETER: Come and look at this star, Inga. It seems to be growing bigger and bigger as I watch.

INGA: Maybe it's just a falling star.

PETER: It's very strange.   It's almost as big as the moon now.   Look, Inga!

INGA: Why, the room does seem to be growing brighter.   Oh!   The star is right over the trees across the road!

PETER: It's coming right at our house, I tell you!

INGA: Let's get away from the window, Peter!

SOUND: (*Light taps on door*)

PETER: (*Frightened*) I wonder what that can be.

INGA: Don't stand there wondering.   Open the door.

PETER: The light is shining in under the door, Inga!   The star — the star is coming into the house through the keyhole!

FAIRY: Good evening, Peter.   Good evening, Inga.

INGA: (*Gasp*) Oh!   The light is taking shape!   Why, it's a lady!

PETER: What a beautiful little lady!   You look like the picture of a fairy.

FAIRY: *Picture* of a fairy?   But I *am* a fairy, Peter.

INGA: Oh!   And I said I didn't believe in fairies!

PETER: Well — well — *I* said I wasn't sure.

FAIRY: Don't look so frightened, both of you.   You have not hurt my feelings.   I will do you no harm.

PETER: Thank you, good fairy.

FAIRY: I have come to prove to you that there really are fairies, and that they really have magic powers.

INGA: Oh, but I do believe in fairies, now that I see you.

PETER: And I'm sure now that there are fairies, because there never was such a lovely, little lady.

FAIRY: Come, come, good people! You still sound afraid of me. I have come to prove that there are fairies by giving you anything you may choose to ask.

INGA: Anything we may ask? Just anything?

FAIRY: Yes, Inga. I'll make it better than just anything. You may have *three* wishes, and they shall all be granted.

INGA: Three wishes!

PETER: How kind you are, good fairy! I shall never again wonder if there are any fairies.

FAIRY: You must be careful, though, in making your wishes. You must wish wisely.

PETER: Of course we will not make our wishes in a hurry. We'll talk it over, my wife and I, and make up our minds what are the best things to wish for.

INGA: And if we make a bad wish the first time, we will still have two more wishes to make up for it.

FAIRY: You had better make every wish a wise one. I'm leaving now, but I shall know what wishes you make. (*Fade*) Goodbye, Inga. Goodbye, Peter.

INGA: Goodbye, good fairy.

PETER: Goodbye, good fairy.

PETER: Well! She's gone again through the keyhole, the way she came. A fairy! A real fairy, who will give us anything we wish! And you said there weren't any fairies, Inga!

INGA: Well, Peter, I'm willing to say I was wrong.

PETER: Now, then, what shall we wish for first?

INGA: Slowly, Peter. Let's think it over carefully, as the fairy said.

PETER: Let's make all three wishes at once.

INGA: No, no! That would never do! Suppose we didn't like what one wish brought? Then we wouldn't be able to change it.

PETER: Maybe you're right, Inga. Maybe we shouldn't use up all three wishes at once. Well, what shall the first one be?

INGA: Let me think a minute.

PETER: How would it do to wish for a fine supper?

INGA: There you go again, thinking of food, as usual. What good would a supper be, no matter how fine? You'd eat it, and it would be gone.

PETER: That's true, Inga. Yes, it would be wiser to ask for something that would last longer. Suppose I ask for a little hand cart, so I won't have to carry those heavy bundles of sticks on my back?

INGA: A hand cart! You lazy thing! Why waste a good wish on a hand cart? It would be better to ask for a new broom for me, so I could get this poor hut clean.

PETER: A broom!   How silly to waste a wish on a broom!
What do you say to asking for a bag of gold pieces?

INGA: That's not a bad idea.   I tell you what, Peter.
Let's have supper first.   That will give us a little more
time to think it over.

PETER: All right.   I'll pull up a chair and sit down.

SOUND: (*Chair moved*)

PETER: What is there to eat?

INGA: I told you before — bread, and cheese, and a few
potatoes baking in the fire.   (*Off mike*) Oh!   Oh!   Oh!

PETER: What's the matter, Inga?   Did you burn your
fingers?

INGA: (*Fade in*) While we were talking, the potatoes have
burned to coal.

PETER: Well!   That leaves just bread and cheese for
supper.

INGA: A fine supper that is!   If only you had sold some
wood before you came home, we might have had something better.

PETER: If we had that bag of gold, we could have bought
something good — a fine sausage, perhaps.   How I
wish I had a fine, big sausage for supper right now!

SOUND: (*Dull, heavy thump on table*)

INGA: What's that?

PETER: Why, it's a big sausage!

INGA: A sausage!   Where did that come from?

PETER: I don't know, I'm sure.

INGA: Oh!   It's your wish, come true, Peter!   You just
wished for a sausage.

PETER: So I did!   I never thought of what I was saying.

INGA: There's our first wish gone.

PETER: I didn't mean it, Inga. Honestly, I didn't.

INGA: What a fool you were to waste a good fairy wish on a sausage!

PETER: I tell you I didn't mean it. It came out without my thinking.

INGA: You *should* have thought of it.

PETER: Well, it can't be helped now. It's done.

INGA: Yes, it's done. Oh, how stupid you are, Peter! Couldn't you have thought of anything better?

PETER: I'm no more stupid than you are.

INGA: It wasn't I who wished for the sausage.

PETER: No, but if I had let you, you would have asked for something even sillier. You wanted a broom.

INGA: What's so silly about a broom? It's useful.

PETER: Not any more useful than the hand cart I wanted to ask for.

INGA: A hand cart! That shows how lazy you are. A person who asks for a broom certainly is not lazy.

PETER: Well, a broom may be useful, but it's a sillier thing to ask for than a sausage.

INGA: Oh, is it? You can't sweep the house with a sausage.

PETER: And you can't eat a broom.

INGA: There you go again, thinking of nothing but eating.

PETER: Stop scolding about it, Inga! If you don't, I'll make the second wish right now, and wish for a second sausage.

INGA: Oh, no, you won't, Peter! *I'm* going to make the next wish, and it won't be for a sausage, I can tell you.

PETER: Stop it, I say! That's all I want to hear about the sausage. I told you I didn't mean to wish for it. You've been so mean about it, I wish that sausage were hanging from the end of your nose.

INGA: Oh, you mean — (*Frightened*) Oh! Oh!

PETER: What's —? (*Frightened*) Oh, Inga!

INGA: The sausage! It's hanging from the end of my nose! Oh, Peter! (*Weeps*)

PETER: The second wish! Fool that I am! I spoke without thinking again! Oh, Inga, my dear! I'm terribly sorry. I didn't mean it. Truly, I didn't mean it.

INGA: Oh! The sausage is so heavy, I can't keep my head up.

PETER: Try to pull it off, Inga.

INGA: I tried. It won't come off! Oh, it won't come off! Whatever shall I do?

PETER: Here, let me try to pull it off.

INGA: Oh, Peter! My nose! Stop! Stop! You're trying to pull my nose off! You're hurting me!

PETER: Perhaps I can chop it off. Where's my axe?

INGA: No, No, Peter! Put down that axe! You'll be chopping my head off! Put down that axe!

PETER: I'll try the big bread knife, Inga. I'll be very careful. (*Pause*) No, it doesn't work.

INGA: Oh, what will become of me? How can I go about with this big sausage on the end of my nose? Everybody will laugh at me.

PETER: I'll tell you what, Inga. Perhaps I can ask for a bag full of gold pieces now.

INGA: What good would a bag of gold pieces be?

PETER: Well, if you're a rich woman, people won't laugh at you — at least, not while you're looking.

INGA: How can I be happy if I know people are laughing at me behind my back?

PETER: Well, you can wear a heavy veil over your face, and nobody will see the sausage.

INGA: How can I see where I'm going if I wear a heavy veil?

PETER: I'll stay with you and lead you.

INGA: And what about your work? Will you go to market for me? And what about Sundays, when we go to church? People will wonder and ask questions, won't they?

PETER: Yes, I can see where that would be hard.

INGA: And besides, this sausage is so long, it hangs down almost to my knees, and it's so heavy, I have to hold my hand on the end of it to keep my head up. (*Weeps*) Oh, dear! Why did you ever make such a wish, Peter?

PETER: It was because you kept nagging at me about wishing for the sausage with our first wish.

INGA: What is to become of me? Oh, what is to become of me? Must I walk about like this, with a sausage on the tip of my nose for the rest of my life?

PETER: I have it, Inga! Our third wish!

INGA: Of course! Our third wish! I've been so upset about this sausage hanging from my nose that I forgot we still have one wish left.

PETER: There's only one thing to wish for with our last wish.

INGA: (*Quickly*) Let *me* do the wishing this time, Peter. I can't take any more chances.

PETER: Go ahead, my dear.

INGA: (*Slowly*) I wish this sausage were back on the table.

SOUND: (*Thud of heavy object on table*)

PETER: There! The sausage is back on the table, Inga.

INGA: Oh! Thank heaven for that!

PETER: Aren't you happy now?

INGA: No, I can't say I'm too happy, Peter.

PETER: But why not?

INGA: We used up three fairy wishes, and all we have to show for them is one sausage.

PETER: Well, that's not too bad. We can have the sausage for several meals. The fairy left us that, at least.

INGA: Yes, but except for that, we are just as poor as we were before. Oh, how the fairy must be laughing at us! It just shows that we'll never get rich by wishing, Peter. We'll have to work for what we want.

MUSIC: (*Up and out*)

ANNOUNCER: And so, boys and girls, ends our story from Sweden, which is called *The Three Wishes*. What would you have wished for if the fairy had given you those three wishes? How the fairy must have laughed at the silly way in which Peter and Inga used their wishes!

Our next tale will be *Lenka's Little House*, a story told to the children of Czechoslovakia.

enka's

CAST   LENKA   STEPMOTHER
            DORLA   OLD MAN
            FATHER   ANNOUNCER
                NARRATOR

SOUNDS

Stones hitting together

Knocks on door

Footsteps on stone

Water flowing

Sound of thunder

Door open

Thud of pail

Little House

ANNOUNCER: It's time for another one of our Tales from the Four Winds. Our story today is one that the children of Czechoslovakia like to hear. The name of the story is *Lenka's Little House*.

MUSIC: (*Up and out*)

NARRATOR: In Czechoslovakia there once lived a woodcutter and his beautiful daughter Lenka. His wife died, and he married another woman who had a daughter of her own, called Dorla. Now Lenka was a good, kind girl, who kept busy all day, while Dorla was lazy and bad-tempered. But the stepmother used to tell the father that it was Lenka, his own child, who was lazy. (*Fade*) One morning, when the woodcutter was getting ready to go to the woods, his wife said to him,

MOTHER: I tell you, husband, your daughter Lenka is a lazy, good-for-nothing girl.

FATHER: Why, it seems to me, that Lenka is always busy around the house when I come home at night.

MOTHER: Yes, that's the only time she works, when she expects you home. I won't stand for her laziness any longer.

FATHER: Well, I'll speak to Lenka about this.

49

MOTHER: Talking won't do any good.   There is only one
  thing to be done.

FATHER: What's that?

MOTHER: You must send her away, out of this house.

FATHER: Send my daughter away!   What are you thinking about?

MOTHER: Let her go and learn to make her own way in
  the world.   She's sixteen, old enough, I'm sure.

FATHER: But how can we be so mean?   How will she get
  along till she finds a place to work?

MOTHER: Oh, I'll give her a bag of bread and meat.   She
  won't starve.

FATHER: No, no!   I can't send my daughter away!

MOTHER: Then I'll do it myself.

FATHER: (*Sigh*) Well, perhaps it will do her good to earn
  her own living.

MOTHER: I'm glad you see it my way at last.   Lenka!
  Lenka!   Where are you, you lazy girl?

LENKA: (*Fade in*) Do you want me?   Here I am.

MOTHER: Why were you playing around outdoors?

LENKA: But you sent me to the well, to get some water.
  Here's the pail.

SOUND: (*Thud of heavy pail on floor*)

MOTHER: Lenka, your father has something to say to you.

LENKA: Yes, Father?

FATHER: We — that is — your mother has decided —

MOTHER: Your father and I think it is time you went out
  to work.

LENKA: You mean, leave our house, and work for somebody else?

MOTHER: Exactly.

LENKA: Oh, Father!

FATHER: Your mother thinks it's best for you to make your own way in the world.

LENKA: Father, do you, too, want me to leave?

FATHER: No. I love you dearly, my child, and I want you with me. But perhaps you will have an easier life with somebody else.

LENKA: But where can I go?

MOTHER: Oh, you'll find a place in the nearby town. You can start out with your father when he leaves for his woodcutting. (*Fade*) I'll put some bread and meat into a bag for you.

LENKA: Oh, Father! Must I leave you?

FATHER: There, there, my child! Don't cry! We'll talk it over on our way to the woods. Go and get the food, and then we'll be on our way.

MUSIC: (*Bridge*)

NARRATOR: The father was very sad as he started for the woods, with Lenka at his side. At the edge of the woods there was a little old hut where the woodcutter often stopped to rest. (*Fade*) When they came to it he said,

FATHER: You must be tired, Lenka, my child. Go into this little house and rest a while.

LENKA: Oh, I'm not a bit tired. We have come only a short way.

FATHER: (*Quickly*) You mustn't walk any farther with me. Better stay here. I'll be back soon.

LENKA: All right. I'll wait here till you come back. Oh, Father! I wish I didn't have to leave you!

FATHER: You'll be happier away from your stepmother. (*Slowly*) Goodbye, my dear child!

LENKA: Oh, but you're coming back in a little while.

FATHER: (*Fade*) Goodbye, my dear child! Goodbye!

MUSIC: (*Bridge*)

NARRATOR: Well, Lenka went into the little house to wait for her father. She waited for hours, but he did not come back. At last she knew that he had left her like that (*Fade*) because he had felt too sad to say a real goodbye.

LENKA: (*Weeps softly*) Oh, dear! I'm all alone now. What shall I do? Where shall I go? (*Weeps*) But whats the use of sitting and crying? It must be nearly noon. I'll eat a bit of the bread and meat my stepmother packed for me, and then start out to look for work. Oh! What's this?

SOUND: (*Noise of stones hitting together*)

LENKA: Two flat stones, and — and ashes, instead of bread and meat! I'm so hungry! What shall I do?

SOUND: (*Knock on door, door open*)

LENKA: Oh! Who are you, little old man?

MAN: (*Small, cheery voice*) God grant you happiness, my child.

LENKA: My name is Lenka. God grant you happiness, too, old man. You look as if you needed good luck. Your clothes are so ragged and old.

MAN: Please, will you wash a poor beggar's face and give him a bite to eat?

LENKA: I wish I could. But there's no water in this hut, and no spring outside. And as for food, my step-mother gave me only ashes and stones.

MAN: If you will look behind this hut, Lenka, you will find a spring of clear water.

LENKA: I'm sure there wasn't any spring near the hut, but I'll look again. I'll take this pitcher from the table with me, (*Fade*) and be right back.

SOUND: (*Footsteps on stone, water flowing, footsteps up and out*)

LENKA: I'm back again, old man. Will you open the door wider for me, please? Thank you. Why! How strange! If you weren't here, old man, just where I left you, I'd think I was dreaming. And yet, you are not where I left you!

MAN: (*Kindly laugh*) I haven't moved from this spot.

LENKA: But when I went out, this room was bare and ugly, with only a table and a chair in it. And now —

MAN: And now, what do you see?

LENKA: A pretty room, with a deep fireplace, and shiny copper pots hanging over the fireplace, and a cupboard filled with lovely dishes. Oh! And a spinning wheel, too, and a big basket full of wool!

MAN: Look through that door, Lenka.

LENKA: (*Slightly off mike*) Oh! Such a pretty bedroom! White curtains at the windows, and a lovely flowered spread on the bed. There was no bedroom before. I wonder how this all happened?

MAN: You will find out later. Now wash my face, child, and let us eat.

LENKA: But I have no food, only the stones and ashes my stepmother gave me.

MAN: Look into your bag again, Lenka.

LENKA: Why, there's bread, and meat, and jam, and some oranges! I wish I could thank the good person who left this here. Come, old man, I'll wash your face, and we'll eat.

MUSIC: (*Bridge*)

55

NARRATOR: So Lenka and the old man sat down and ate the good food that now came out of the bag. Later, the old man sat in the sun while the girl cleaned up the room and then worked at the spinning wheel. (*Fade*) When night came, Lenka said to the old man,

LENKA: You are old and tired, old man. You must take the bed for the night. I'll make myself comfortable in the chair by the fireplace.

MAN: You are very kind to a poor old beggar, my child.

LENKA: I'm not better than a beggar myself. Good night, and pleasant dreams, old man.

MUSIC: (*Bridge*)

NARRATOR: So Lenka made herself as comfortable as she could in the chair by the fireplace. She had had such a tiring day that she was soon fast asleep.

NARRATOR: At midnight she was awakened by a loud, rumbling noise like thunder.

SOUND: (*Thunder*)

NARRATOR: Then she heard her name called. It sounded as if the voice were coming from the floor.

MAN: Lenka! Lenka! I'm down here!

LENKA: Who's calling? Oh! There you are! Why, I never saw such a tiny little man. You're not more than a foot high.

MAN: Are you sure you never saw me before?

LENKA: Oh! With your long, white beard, you do look like the old beggar man in the next room. But he is much bigger than you.

MAN: I was that beggar man. I am really a brownie, and I can change my shape anytime I wish to.

LENKA: A brownie!

MAN: Because you were kind to a poor beggar, I changed this tumble-down hut into a pretty place for you to live in.

LENKA: Oh, so it is you I have to thank for everything!

MAN: And I have a gift for you, in this bag.

LENKA: A gift?   The bag looks very heavy.

MAN: It is full of gold and jewels, from my home down under the ground.   Now you will never have to worry about food or a house to live in.

LENKA: Gold and jewels, for me?

MAN: And in the bedroom you will find some pretty dresses.

LENKA: How can I ever thank you enough for all your kindness, little man?

MAN: It is your reward for being kind to the poor and hungry.

LENKA: You must come here often, good brownie, and —

SOUND: (*Thunder*)

LENKA: Why, he's gone!   The brownie is gone!

MUSIC: (*Bridge*)

NARRATOR: And what about Lenka's father all this time? Well, he felt very sad, you may be sure. Early the next day he set out for the hut where he had left his daughter. What was his surprise, as he came near the spot, to find that the old hut was gone! In its place he saw a pretty little cottage, covered with climbing roses. When he came nearer he heard Lenka singing.

MUSIC: (*Folk song*)

FATHER: Lenka! Lenka, my child!

MUSIC: (*Out on folk song*)

LENKA: Father! Oh, Father!

FATHER: How glad I am to see you so well and happy! I have been so worried about you.

LENKA: Well, you need not worry about me any more. Look at this pretty little house.

FATHER: But this used to be a poor, tumble-down hut. How did it change so?

LENKA: An old beggar man came by yesterday, and asked me to wash his face and give him some food. I did, and — well, he turned out to be a brownie. He changed the hut into this pretty cottage, and he gave me a bag of gold and jewels, too. Look, Father!

FATHER: How wonderful for you, my child!

LENKA: You must take all the jewels for yourself, Father, and most of the gold, too.

FATHER: Oh, no! I couldn't take it. The brownie gave it to you.

LENKA: But I really don't need much. I can live on just a little of the gold, until I start selling the yarn I spin.

FATHER: Well, I'll take it, but I'll hide most of it away for you.

58

LENKA: Sit and watch me spin for a while, Father, before you go on to your work.

MUSIC: (*Folk tune as bridge*)

NARRATOR: When Lenka's father came home that night, he told his wife and her daughter what had happened to Lenka. (*Fade*) His wife was very angry, and said,

MOTHER: That's just like you, to do such a fine thing for your own daughter. A pretty house, and a bag of gold and jewels!

FATHER: But it wasn't I who did it. It was the kind brownie.

MOTHER: To-morrow you must take my daughter Dorla to the woods and see that she gets a pretty house, too. Do you hear me? I'll not have that Lenka of yours get all the pretty things, (*Fade*) while my own daughter Dorla —.

MUSIC: (*Bridge*)

NARRATOR: Well, the next day the father took Dorla to the forest and built a tiny hut for her. As Dorla sat in the open door of the hut, eating the good lunch her mother had given her, (*Fade*) the little old beggar man came along.

MAN: Please, my child, will you wash a poor beggar's face and give him a bite to eat?

DORLA: Wash your face, indeed! Be off with you.

MAN: I'm so hungry. Won't you give me just a little of your food?

DORLA: Why should I? Go and beg somewhere else.

MAN: You are not very kind to a poor, hungry man.

DORLA: And why should I be kind to a beggar like you? Be off, or I'll beat you with this stick!

MAN: Oho! So that's the sort of girl you are, bad-tempered and unkind! Well, you shall have your reward.

DORLA: Oh! Let go of me! Where are you dragging me? Let me go! I'll crash against that tree! Oh! The ground under the tree is opening!

MAN: Yes, Dorla, I'm taking you down under the ground, to the home of the brownies. There you'll stay, and work for the brownies for the rest of your life.

MUSIC: (*Bridge*)

NARRATOR: So the little beggar man, who was really a brownie, took the lazy Dorla down under the ground, and nobody ever saw her again. But Lenka lived happily in her pretty cottage, where her father often came to visit her. By and by a rich man's son came by and saw the beautiful Lenka, and married her.

MUSIC: (*Up and out*)

ANNOUNCER: And so, boys and girls, ends *Lenka's Little House*, our story from Czechoslovakia. It made Lenka sad to leave her father's house, but her kindness brought her a better house, all for herself. As for the bad-tempered Dorla, I'm sure that only her mother was sorry when Dorla was carried off by the brownie.

Be sure to listen to our next story, called *The Straw Ox*. It is a tale that the children of Russia like to hear.

he Straw

CAST   OLD MAN   WOLF
              OLD WOMAN FOX
              OX   RABBIT
              BEAR   ANNOUNCER
                    NARRATOR

SOUNDS

Animal sounds

Thud

Knock on door

Steel on stone

Door opened and closed

Ox

ANNOUNCER: Today you will hear a story from Russia. The story is called *The Straw Ox*. Now, an ox is a very useful animal, but would you think anyone would want one made of straw? Listen to our story and you will find out.

MUSIC: (*Up and out*)

NARRATOR: Once upon a time in Russia there lived a poor old man and his wife. The man earned very little, and they were often hungry. (*Fade*) One day, when they had no food or money, the old woman said to her husband,

WIFE: I want you to do something for me, husband.

MAN: Anything you want, wife, so long as it costs no money.

WIFE: Make me an ox out of straw, and cover it all over with tar.

MAN: How silly! What's the good of a straw ox covered with tar?

WIFE: Never mind. You just make it for me.

MAN: (*Fade*) Silly idea! A straw ox!

MUSIC: (*Bridge*)

NARRATOR: Though he did think it was silly, the old man made an ox out of straw and smeared it with tar. Early the next morning the old woman took the straw ox out to the fields and (*Fade*) sat down under a tree and said,

WIFE: Eat your grass, little ox, while I spin my flax. (*Fade*) Eat your grass, little ox, while I spin my flax.

NARRATOR: The old woman sat under the tree and spun her flax. By and by she grew tired and fell asleep. While she was sleeping a big bear came pad-pad out of the woods and rushed at the straw ox. But the bear soon stopped short in surprise. (*Fade*) He said to the straw ox,

BEAR: What a strange animal you are! I never saw anything like you before. Who are you?

OX: I am an ox, I am, made of straw and covered with tar.

BEAR: Oh! Made of straw and covered with tar, are you? Then give me some of your tar to mend my fur. I tore it when I climbed a tree to get some honey.

OX: Take as much as you like, Mr. Bear.

BEAR: Thank you. I will. (*Grunts*) Mmm! Uh! Oh! I can't pull my paw away! Let go of me, little ox! Let go, I say, or I'll hit you with my other paw! Oh! Now both my front paws are stuck fast! Let go of me, or I'll bite you, little ox! You won't? Then I *will* bite — Ow! (*Growl with mouth closed*)

NARRATOR: You see, when the bear tried to bite the straw ox, his nose and mouth stuck to the tar. All the bear could do was growl at the back of his throat, while he pulled and pulled to get away.

MUSIC: (*Bridge*)

64

NARRATOR: Well, in a little while the old woman woke up and looked around. There was no ox to be seen, so she hurried home. There she found the straw ox, with the bear stuck fast to its side, standing outside the cellar door. (*Fade*) The old woman called out,

WIFE: Husband! Husband! Come out here, quickly!

MAN: (*Fade in*) What is it, wife? What's wrong?

WIFE: Nothing's wrong. Look! The little straw ox has brought us a bear.

MAN: A bear, as I live!

WIFE: What shall we do with it?

MAN: I'll have to think. While I'm thinking what to do, I'll tie his feet together — like this — and pull him away from the little straw ox — like this. Now I'll throw Mr. Bear down into the cellar — like that!

SOUND: (*Door open, thud of heavy body, door slammed*)

MAN: Stay there, Mr. Bear, till I make up my mind what to do with you.

MUSIC: (*Bridge*)

NARRATOR: The next morning the old woman took her flax and drove the little straw ox to the fields again. She sat down under a tree and said to the ox,

WIFE: Eat your grass, little ox, while I spin my flax. (*Fade*) Eat your grass, little ox, while I spin my flax.

NARRATOR: The old woman spun her flax. By and by she grew tired and fell asleep. Soon a gray wolf came rushing out of the woods. He stopped in surprise when he saw the little straw ox, (*Fade*) and said,

WOLF: You are a strange animal. I never saw anything like you before. Who are you?

OX: I am an ox, I am, made of straw and covered with tar.

WOLF: Oh! Made of straw and covered with tar, are you? Then give me some of your tar to mend my fur where the dogs tore it.

OX: Take as much as you like, Gray Wolf.

WOLF: Thank you. I will. (*Grunts*) Mmm! Uh! I can't pull my paw away! Let go of me, little ox! Let go, or I'll hit you with my other paw! Oh! Now both my paws are stuck fast! Let go of me, little ox, or I'll bite you! You won't? Then I *will* bite you! Ow! (*Fading growl*)

NARRATOR: Well, when the gray wolf tried to bite the straw ox, his nose and mouth stuck fast to the tar on the side of the ox. All the wolf could do was growl at the back of his throat while he pulled and pulled to get away.

MUSIC: (*Bridge*)

66

NARRATOR: In a little while the old woman woke up. She looked around, but there was no little ox to be seen, so she went home. There, by the fence outside her house, stood the little straw ox with the gray wolf stuck fast to its side. (*Fade*) The old woman called out,

WIFE: Husband! Husband! Come out here, quickly!

MAN: (*Fade in*) What is it, wife? What's wrong?

WIFE: Nothing's wrong, husband. Look! The little straw ox has brought us a gray wolf.

MAN: A gray wolf, as I live!

WIFE: What shall we do with the wolf?

MAN: I'll have to think. While I'm thinking what to do, I'll tie his feet together — like this — and pull him away from the ox — like this. Now I'll throw Mr. Gray Wolf down into the cellar — like that!

SOUND: (*Door open, thud of heavy body, door slammed*)

MAN: Stay there, Mr. Wolf, while I make up my mind what to do with you.

MUSIC: (*Bridge*)

NARRATOR: Well, the next morning the old woman drove her little straw ox out to the fields again. This time the little ox brought home a red fox stuck to its tarred sides. The old man threw the fox into the cellar, too. On the fourth day the ox brought home a rabbit, which also went into the cellar, along with the bear, the wolf, and the fox. Then the old man sat down outside the cellar door to think.

MUSIC: (*Bridge*)

NARRATOR: Well, the old man didn't think long. Pretty soon he went into the house and came back with a long knife, which he started sharpening on a stone.

SOUND: (*Steel on stone*)

NARRATOR: Through the cellar window the bear saw the old man sharpening his knife and called out,

BEAR: Tell me, old man, why are you sharpening that knife?

MAN: I'm making it very sharp so I can take off your skin, Mr. Bear.

BEAR: Take off my skin! Oh! Oh! What do you want it for?

MAN: I'll make a coat for myself and a coat for my old wife out of your skin.

BEAR: Oh, please don't take off my skin, old man! Let me go, and I'll bring you a fine present.

MAN: What can you bring me, Mr. Bear?

BEAR: Do you and your old wife like honey?

MAN: Honey! Mmm! Yes, we both like honey very much.

BEAR: Then let me go, old man, and I'll bring you a whole beehive full of honey.

MAN: Very well, I'll let you go, Mr. Bear. But be sure you bring me the honey. I'm coming down to set you free.

MUSIC: (*Bridge*)

NARRATOR: After the old man had set the bear free, he sat down on the bench outside the cellar window again and began to sharpen his knife.

SOUND: (*Steel on stone*)

NARRATOR: The wolf saw this, and called out,

WOLF: Old man, what are you sharpening your knife for?

MAN: So I can take off your skin, Gray Wolf.

WOLF: Take off my skin! Oh! Oh! What will you do with it?

MAN: I'll make a warm cap for myself and one for my wife out of your skin.

WOLF: Oh, please don't skin me, old man! Let me go, and I'll bring you a fine present.

MAN: What can you bring me, Gray Wolf?

WOLF: I'll bring you a whole flock of sheep.

MAN: A flock of sheep! Well, that would be useful. Yes, I'll let you go. I'm coming down to set you free, but be sure to bring me some sheep.

MUSIC: (*Bridge*)

NARRATOR: Well, after he had freed the wolf, the old man began to sharpen his knife again.

SOUND: (*Steel on stone*)

NARRATOR: The fox heard him and called out,

FOX: What are you doing, old man?

MAN: I'm sharpening my knife to skin you, Red Fox.

FOX: Oh, no, no! Why should you want to skin me?

MAN: I want your fur to make a collar and cuffs for my coat and my old wife's coat.

FOX: Oh, please don't skin me, old man. If you'll let me go, I'll bring you a present.

MAN: A present? What sort of present?

FOX: How would you like some hens, and ducks, and geese?

MAN: Hens, and ducks, and geese! Hm! I could sell their eggs, and have a roast goose for Christmas. Yes, I'd like some hens, and ducks, and geese. I'll let you go, Red Fox, but don't forget your promise.

MUSIC: (*Bridge*)

NARRATOR: Well, now the cellar was empty, except for the rabbit. The old man began to sharpen his knife again.

SOUND: (*Steel on stone*)

NARRATOR: The little rabbit called out through the cellar window,

RABBIT: Old man, why are you sharpening your knife?

MAN: I'm going to take off your skin, Little Rabbit.

RABBIT: Take off my skin! Oh, no, no! What can you do with my skin? I'm such a little animal.

MAN: Little rabbits have nice, soft, warm skins. I can make mittens for myself and my old wife out of your skin, Little Rabbit. Then our hands will be warm in the cold frosts of the Russian winters.

RABBIT: Oh, please, old man, don't take off my skin! Don't take off my skin! Let me go, and I'll bring you a fine present.

MAN: And what can you bring me, Little Rabbit?

RABBIT: I can bring you vegetables —
nice fresh lettuce, carrots, cabbage, and spinach.

MAN: Fresh vegetables! Yes, my wife and I would
certainly like some vegetables. We have been too poor
to buy any for a long time. Very well, Little Rabbit.
I'll let you go if you'll bring me some fresh vegetables.

RABBIT: I promise, old man. Oh, I'll surely bring you
some. Only don't skin me! Let me go!

MAN: I'm coming down to set you free, Little Rabbit.

MUSIC: (*Bridge*)

NARRATOR: And so the old man set all the animals free —
the bear, and the gray wolf, and the red fox, and the
little rabbit. He told his wife what each animal had
promised to bring. You remember, don't you? The
bear promised to come back with some honey, the wolf
said he'd bring a whole flock of sheep, the fox promised
some hens, and ducks, and geese, and the little rabbit
said he'd bring some fresh vegetables. Well, all afternoon the old man and the old woman sat out in front
of the house, waiting for the animals to come back.
When it grew dark, the old couple ate some dry bread
and went to bed. Very early the next morning, before
the sun was up, there was a loud knock on the door.

SOUND: (*Knock*)

NARRATOR: The old woman sat up in bed (*Fade*) and cried
out to her husband,

71

WIFE: Wake up, husband!　There's somebody at the door.

MAN: I'll go and see who it is.

SOUND: (*Door open*)

MAN: Well, Well!　The bear is running away from the door.　He's left a whole beehive on the doorstep.　All that honey!　Mmm!　This tastes sweet, this honey does!

WIFE: (*Off mike*) Stop eating that honey!　Can't you wait till breakfast time?　It's still dark.　Get back to sleep!

MAN: You're right, wife.

SOUND: (*Door shut*)

MAN: I'm coming back to bed.　But that honey is good.

SOUND: (*Knock on door*)

MAN: Now, who can that be?

WIFE: There's a good way to find out.　Open the door.

MAN: (*Grunts*) Why didn't he come before I got back to bed, whoever he is?

SOUND: (*Door open, baa of sheep up and under*)

MAN: Why, it's the gray wolf running away from the door.　Listen, wife.　What do you hear?

SOUND: (*Baa of sheep, up and under*)

WIFE: (*Fade in*) Sheep!　Wait!　I'm coming to see them.　Oh!　A whole flock of sheep!

MAN: Yes, the gray wolf has kept his promise and brought us a whole flock of sheep.

SOUND: (*Out on sheep*)

MAN: Ah!　They're quiet, now that the wolf has gone.

WIFE: Oh!　Oh!　What do I see?

SOUND: (*Noise of ducks, hens, and geese*)

WIFE: The red fox is driving hens, and ducks, and geese into our yard!

MAN: Wonderful!

SOUND: (*Out on noise of hens, ducks, and geese*)

MAN: How they quiet down when the fox is out of sight!

WIFE: And here comes the little rabbit, dragging a load of fresh vegetables — lettuce, and spinach, and carrots, and cabbage. My! Now we need never be hungry again.

MAN: No, now we need never be hungry again. That idea of yours, wife, a little ox made out of straw and covered all over with tar, was not such a silly idea, after all.

MUSIC: (*Bridge*)

NARRATOR: Well, the old man and the old woman ate the honey and the fresh vegetables, and they sold the flock of sheep and most of the hens, and ducks, and geese. Now they had all the money they needed, and they were very happy.

As for the little straw ox, it stood in the sun by the fence till it dried up and fell to pieces, and the wind blew the pieces away.

MUSIC: (*Up and out*)

ANNOUNCER: And so ends the story of *The Straw Ox*. Now you know that the old woman was not really silly when she asked for an ox made of straw. The old man must have been glad that he made the ox for her.

Be sure to listen to our next story which comes from Denmark. It is called *What the Good Man Does Is Right*.

73

What the Good

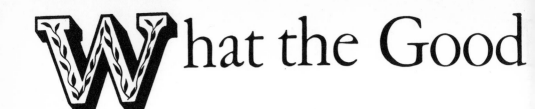

CAST

OLD MAN	SECOND YOUNG MAN
OLD WOMAN	WAITER
FARMER	STRANGER
SHEPHERD	ANNOUNCER
FIRST YOUNG MAN	NARRATOR

SOUNDS

Animal sounds

Carriage wheels

Hoof beats

Clink of gold pieces

Man Does Is Right

ANNOUNCER: Hello, boys and girls! It's time for another one of the Tales from the Four Winds. The story you will hear today comes from Denmark. The name of the story is *What the Good Man Does Is Right*.

MUSIC: (*Up and out*)

NARRATOR: Once upon a time an old man and his old wife lived in a little old farmhouse in Denmark. The old man and his wife had very little, but they were happy. There were ducks swimming in the pond, and there was a horse that ate the grass by the roadside. Now the horse was the one thing that the old man and his wife had little use for. Sometimes the old man rode into town on it, but not often. (*Fade*) They were talking about the horse one day.

MAN: That horse of ours gets fatter and lazier every day, wife.

WOMAN: No wonder! All he does is eat the good grass in summer and the sweet hay in the winter.

MAN: We don't have enough use for him. Perhaps we should sell him.

WOMAN: That's a good idea, husband.

MAN: Or perhaps we should exchange him for something more useful.

75

WOMAN: That's an even better idea. You always know just the right thing to do.

MAN: Today is market day. I'll ride the horse into town and sell him or exchange him. What more useful thing shall I get instead?

WOMAN: I don't know, I'm sure. I'll leave it to you. Whatever you do will be right.

MAN: You're the best wife a man ever had! I'll start for town right now.

WOMAN: Wait a minute. Let me fix your tie. There! Now you look fine. Goodbye, old man.

MAN: Goodbye, wife. I'll be back as soon as I can.

MUSIC: (*Gay, as for a fair*)

NARRATOR: So the old man got on his horse and started for town. The road was crowded with people riding, driving, or walking to market. Some were leading animals to be sold.

SOUND: (*Animal sounds*)

NARRATOR: Soon the old man came alongside a farmer leading a cow.

SOUND: (*Moo of cow*)

NARRATOR: (*Fade*) The old man greeted the farmer.

MAN: Good morning, friend farmer.

FARMER: Good morning to you, old man.

MAN: That's a fine cow you have there.

SOUND: (*Moo of cow*)

FARMER: She's a very fine cow.

MAN: Does she give plenty of milk?

FARMER: She's the best milker of all the cows around here. I ought to get a very good price for her at the market.

MAN: She would be a good cow for my old wife and me.

FARMER: This cow is very gentle.   Your old wife would have no trouble milking her.

MAN: And my wife could churn butter and make cheese from the milk.

FARMER: Yes, she could.   Why don't you buy my cow, old man?

MAN: I haven't any money, only this horse.

FARMER: That's too bad!   This horse of yours, now —

MAN: He's not as lazy as he looks.   It's just that I don't use him often enough.   Will you take him for your cow?

FARMER: It's a bargain!   I'll take your horse in exchange.

MAN: I'll get down.   (*Grunts*) Aaah!   There you are!

FARMER: And here's your cow.

SOUND: (*Moo of cow*)

FARMER: You can take her right home with you now.

MAN: Well, I started out for the market, so I may as well go and look around to see what I can see.

FARMER: Then I may see you later. I'll ride in. (*Fade*) Get up! Get up!

MUSIC: (*Bridge*)

NARRATOR: The old man walked on with his cow. Soon he came alongside a shepherd driving a sheep to market.

SOUND: (*Baa of sheep*)

NARRATOR: The old man looked at the sheep, and a thought came into his head. (*Fade*) He spoke to the shepherd.

MAN: Good morning, friend shepherd.

SHEPHERD: Good morning, old man.

MAN: That's a fine, fat sheep you have there.

SHEPHERD: Indeed it is. Feel how thick and soft its wool is. It's ready to be sheared.

MAN: That would be a fine sheep for my wife and me to have.

SHEPHERD: It would, old man, a better animal than your cow. The cow gives milk, to be sure, but she often kicks over the pail, and then you have nothing.

MAN: That's true. The sheep could eat the grass by our fence, and it is small enough to be kept in the house in winter.

SHEPHERD: And look at all the wool you would shear every spring.

MAN: That's true.   My old wife would have enough wool for coats and mittens for the two of us.

SHEPHERD: Well, why don't you buy my sheep, old man?

MAN: I haven't any money, only this cow.

SHEPHERD: Well, let's see.   This cow of yours, now —

MAN: She's a very good milker, and if you take her in exchange for your sheep, you'll have my great thanks as well.

SHEPHERD: I'll do it for you, old man.   Here's my sheep.

SOUND: (*Baa of sheep*)

MAN: And here's my cow, shepherd.

SOUND: (*Moo of cow*)

MAN: Many thanks to you.

SHEPHERD: Your wife will be glad to see you bringing this fine, fat sheep home, old man.

MAN: Oh, I'm not going home yet.   I started for the market, so I might as well keep on.

SHEPHERD: Well, I'm younger than you, and I walk faster.   I'll see you in town later, old man.   Goodbye!

MUSIC: (*Bridge*)

NARRATOR: The old man walked on, leading his sheep. By and by a young man came cutting across the fields into the road.   He was carrying a large goose under his arm.   (*Fade*) He greeted the old man politely.

FIRST YOUNG MAN: Good morning, old man.

MAN: Good morning to you, young man.   Are you going to market?

FIRST YOUNG MAN: Yes.   I'm going to sell this goose!

MAN: My!   It's a fine, fat goose!

79

FIRST YOUNG MAN: I've been fattening it for weeks.

MAN: My old wife would like this bird. How often she has said, "If we only had a goose swimming in our pond!"

FIRST YOUNG MAN: This goose would be delicious roasted, sir.

MAN: Mmm! Yes! And think of all the sweet goose fat we could have to spread on our bread.

FIRST YOUNG MAN: And look at her thick, soft feathers, old man.

MAN: My old wife could stuff a feather bed to keep us warm in the winter.

FIRST YOUNG MAN: Why don't you buy my goose?

MAN: I'd like to, but I have no money, only this sheep. If you'd take this sheep for your goose —

FIRST YOUNG MAN: Well, I don't know. What would I do with one sheep?

MAN: You could shear it and have your mother make you a warm jacket and mittens.

FIRST YOUNG MAN: Well, I'll do it for you, old man. Take my goose.

MAN: And here's my sheep.

FIRST YOUNG MAN: Your old wife will be glad to see this fine, fat goose.

MAN: Oh, I'm not going right home. I started for market, so I might as well keep on.

FIRST YOUNG MAN: In that case, I may see you later, old man. Goodbye!

MUSIC: (*Bridge*)

NARRATOR: By this time the old man was near the town. The road was getting more and more crowded with people and animals.

SOUND: (*Animal sounds in briefly*)

NARRATOR: He had to walk slowly. Up from behind him came another young man, carrying a hen under his arm.

SOUND: (*Cluck of hen*)

NARRATOR: The old man turned around when he heard the hen clucking.

MAN: Good morning, young man.

SECOND YOUNG MAN: Good morning to you, old man.

MAN: That's a fine hen you have there, young man, the finest I've seen in many a month.

SECOND YOUNG MAN: She is a fine bird, old man. I've been stuffing her with corn till she's ready to burst.

MAN: Mmm! My old wife and I like roast chicken almost as much as we like roast goose.

SECOND YOUNG MAN: Are you going to sell that goose at the market?

MAN: Oh, no!   I just got this goose.   I took it in exchange for my sheep.

SECOND YOUNG MAN: You gave your sheep for a goose? What a good bargainer you are!

MAN: *I* think so!   A goose isn't so hard to care for as a sheep.   A sheep really needs a meadow to graze in, while a goose can eat the grass by our fence.

SECOND YOUNG MAN: Well now, old man, just look at this hen of mine.   It eats even less than a goose.

MAN: That's true.

SECOND YOUNG MAN: A hen can always pick up a grain of wheat somewhere.   A hen eats worms, too, which she digs out of the ground.   Those wouldn't cost you anything.

MAN: That's true.

SECOND YOUNG MAN: And don't forget, old man, that a hen lays eggs for you.

MAN: Yes, *that's* true.   I can set her on the eggs and get more chickens.   Young man, will you take my goose in exchange for your hen?   I'll be very grateful to you.

SECOND YOUNG MAN: Well, I wouldn't do it for everybody, old man, but I'll do it for you.   Here's my hen.

SOUND: (*Cluck of hen*)

MAN: And here's my fine, white goose,
and thank you very much.

SECOND YOUNG MAN: Don't mention it! Your old wife, too, will thank me, when she sees this hen.

MAN: Oh, I'm not going right home. I've done so much clever bargaining, exchanging one thing for another, that I'm hot, and tired, and hungry. I'll step into this inn across the road and have a bite to eat before going home.

SECOND YOUNG MAN: In that case, I'll be on my way. Goodbye, old man!

MAN: Goodbye, and thank you again, young man.

WAITER: (*Fade in*) Here! Here! Why don't you look where you're going, old man?

MAN: Oh! Excuse me, waiter! I didn't see you.

WAITER: You almost made me drop this sack.

MAN: That sack looks very heavy. What's in it?

WAITER: Rotten apples. A whole sackful of rotten apples.

MAN: What are you going to do with them?

WAITER: Why, feed them to the pigs, of course.

MAN: Feed them to the pigs! Such a waste of good rotten apples!

WAITER: What else would you expect me to do with them, old man?

MAN: I wish my old wife could see all these rotten apples. Last year the old tree by our pond had only one single apple on it.

WAITER: That was too bad, old man. And what did you and your wife do with the one apple?

MAN: We were so happy to have it, we kept it in the cupboard till it was quite spoiled and rotten. And here you have a whole bagful of rotten apples. How I wish my old wife could see them!

WAITER: Well, I'll sell you the apples. What will you give me for the whole sackful?

MAN: Why, I'll give you my fine hen for them.

WAITER: All right! It's a bargain. Here are the apples.

MAN: And here's the hen.

SOUND: (*Clucking of hen*)

MAN: Don't let her get away. I'm going inside to get a bite to eat.

MUSIC: (*Bridge*)

NARRATOR: The old man went into the inn, carrying the sack of apples. He looked around for a place to put the bag, and then put it in a corner by the fireplace. Since it was market day, the inn was crowded, so the old man had to sit at a table with a stranger. Now in those days, you know, people had to have a fire, even on the hottest day, because they cooked their food in pots over the fire. Pretty soon the bag of apples started baking. (*Fade*) The stranger sniffed and said to the old man,

STRANGER: Hummm! What is that smell?

MAN: What kind of smell do you mean, sir?

STRANGER: It smells like roasting apples, but not very good ones.

MAN: You're right, sir. Those are my apples, and they *are* rotten. I have a whole sackful, in the corner by the fireplace.

STRANGER: A whole sackful of rotten apples! Where did you get them, old man?

MAN: I gave a fine hen for them.

STRANGER: A hen for a bag of rotten apples! Where did you get the hen?

MAN: Oh, I gave a fine, fat goose for it.

STRANGER: And what did you give for the goose?

MAN: For that I gave a sheep.

STRANGER: And what did you pay for the sheep?

MAN: Oh, I gave a cow for it.

STRANGER: It gets better and better! And what did you give for the cow?

MAN: Oh, I gave our horse for the cow.

STRANGER: A horse for a cow!

MAN: You see, sir, my wife and I didn't use him much, so we decided to exchange him for something more useful.

STRANGER: (*Laughs*) Well! So you have nothing but a bagful of rotten apples for your horse! Your wife will certainly give you a scolding when you get home!

MAN: (*Laughs*) My wife, scold *me?* I should say not! She'll only hug me and say, "What the good man does is always right."

STRANGER: I don't believe that.

MAN: But it's true.

STRANGER: I'll bet you a hundred pieces of gold that she'll scold you.

MAN: I have no gold, sir, but I'll bet you a hundred of my rotten apples that my wife will not scold me.

STRANGER: Good! I have a carriage outside the inn. I'll go home with you and see what happens. Let's go, old man.

SOUND: (*Hoof beats and carriage wheels up and out*)

MAN: Stop, sir. Here's my little house, and there's my old wife, sitting and waiting for me. I'll get out of the carriage first. (*Pause*) Well, I'm back from market, wife.

WOMAN: I'm glad you're back, husband. What did you get for our horse?

MAN: I exchanged it for a cow.

WOMAN: A cow! That's fine! Now we shall have milk, and butter, and cheese. That was a good bargain.

MAN: Oh, but I gave the cow for a sheep.

WOMAN: Ah! That's better still. Now we can have wool jackets and stockings in winter. You did just right, husband.

MAN: Yes, but I gave the sheep for a fat goose.

WOMAN: A goose! That's wonderful of you, old man! Now we can have roast goose, and goose fat for our bread. You're always thinking how to please me!

MAN: But I gave the goose for a hen.

WOMAN: A hen! Think of that! The hen will lay eggs, and we shall have more chickens. Just what I always wished for!

MAN: Yes, wife, but I gave the hen for a sackful of rotten apples.

WOMAN: A whole sackful of rotten apples! Oh, I must hug you for that, husband! After you left this morning, I went across the road to Mrs. Brown, to borrow an onion. But she said nothing at all grows in her garden, not even a rotten apple. She hasn't even *one* rotten apple, and here you bring me a whole sackful! My good husband always does the right thing!

STRANGER: (*Laughs*) Well! I wouldn't believe it if I didn't hear it with my own ears! I don't mind losing a bet to such a happy pair. Here are your hundred pieces of gold, old man.

SOUND: (*Clink of gold pieces*)

STRANGER: And you, old woman, may you and your husband live happily together for a long time, and may you always believe that what the good man does is right.

MUSIC: (*Up and out*)

ANNOUNCER: And so ends our tale from Denmark, *What the Good Man Does Is Right*. Do you think a bagful of rotten apples was a good exchange for a horse?

Listen to our next story, *Jack and the Beanstalk*. It is an old tale from England.

ack and the

CAST JACK GIANT
MOTHER GIANT'S WIFE
FARMER ANNOUNCER
NARRATOR

SOUNDS

Chairs moved about

Rattle of beans

Rattle of dishes

Metal cover on pot

Heavy footsteps

Axe chopping

Door open and shut

Snores

Animal sounds

Knock

Beanstalk

ANNOUNCER: Today you will hear a story that the children of England have liked for years and years. Children in America know this old tale too. It is *Jack and the Beanstalk*.

MUSIC: (*Up and out*)

NARRATOR: Once upon a time in a small village in England there lived a poor woman. She had only one child, a good-natured but lazy boy whose name was Jack. Instead of making him go to work, (*Fade*) she only scolded him for being lazy all the time.

MOTHER: Jack! Jack! Where are you, you lazy boy? Jack!

JACK: (*Off mike*) Do you want me, Mother?

MOTHER: Come here at once!

SOUND: (*Door open and shut*)

JACK: (*Fade in*) Here I am, Mother. What is it?

MOTHER: What were you doing out there? I couldn't see you through the window.

JACK: I was watching the farmers driving their animals to the village market.

MOTHER: That's just like you! You keep busy watching other people work. Why don't *you* go to work?

JACK: I can't think of anything I want to do.

MOTHER: Oh, it's all my own fault! I've spoiled you. I should have made you go to work long ago. Now we're so poor we haven't a thing to eat in the house.

JACK: Oh, Mother! You make me feel so sorry! I'll find some work next week.

MOTHER: Next week! That's what you keep saying all the time. Are we to starve till then?

JACK: Isn't there something we can sell, Mother, to get food?

MOTHER: We have nothing left but our cow. I don't like to sell her, but I don't see what else to do.

JACK: Oh, Mother! Do let me take her to the market and sell her for you!

MOTHER: You, Jack? You haven't sense enough to make a good bargain.

JACK: Oh, I'll be very careful and very clever. Do let me go!

MOTHER: (*Sigh*) I suppose I'll have to. I'm too old to make the trip myself, driving a cow before me.

JACK: Thank you, Mother! (*Fade*) Wait till you see how much money I'll bring back!

MUSIC: (*Bridge*)

NARRATOR: So Jack took the cow and went whistling down the road.

JACK: (*Whistles short tune*)

SOUND: (*Cow moos*)

JACK: Whoa, there, Bossy! Keep to your own side of the road. Good morning, friend farmer.

FARMER: Good morning, my lad. Where are you going with that cow?

JACK: I'm going to sell her in the village.

FARMER: Is that so? Well, I can see by your face that you're a clever fellow, and will drive a good bargain. Look at these beans I have in my hat here.

SOUND: (*Rattle of dry beans*)

JACK: My! How very large they are! And such a queer color!

FARMER: Well, if you're going to sell your cow, why not sell her to me? I'll give you all these beans for her.

JACK: Mmm! They're very large beans, and such a lot of them. All right. It's a deal. Take my cow. I'll run right home with these beans and show my mother what a fine bargain I've made.

SOUND: (*Moo of cow*)

MUSIC: (*Bridge*)

SOUND: (*Door open*)

JACK: (*Fade in*) Mother! Oh, Mother! Look what I brought back for the cow!

MOTHER: Goodness! Don't burst into a room like that, Jack! Close the door.

SOUND: (*Door closed*)

MOTHER: Did you sell our cow?

JACK: Yes, Mother. I could hardly wait till I got home to show you what I got for her. Look!

SOUND: (*Rattle of beans*)

MOTHER: What? This hatful of beans?

JACK: Yes. Aren't they big? Did you ever see such strange-looking beans?

MOTHER: A hatful of dried beans for my good cow! (*Weeps*) Oh, Jack! Jack! How could you be so stupid?

JACK: But, Mother! So many of them! Aren't they a good bargain?

MOTHER: (*Angry*) Beans! Take them out of my sight, you good-for-nothing boy! Out the window with those beans!

JACK: Mother! You threw away those lovely beans! You might have cooked them for our supper.

MOTHER: Cook those queer-looking beans? No, indeed! And we have nothing else for supper, not even milk. We'll have to go to bed hungry. (*Cries*) Oh, dear! Oh, dear!

MUSIC: (*Bridge*)

NARRATOR: The next morning when Jack woke up, he thought it was very dark. He went to his window, but he could not see out of it. It was covered with something green. He ran out into the garden. There he saw a strange sight. (*Fade*) He called out to his mother,

JACK: Mother! Mother!

MOTHER: (*Off mike*) What is it, Jack? It's still very early. Where are you?

JACK: I'm out in the garden. Throw a coat on, and come out here, quickly, Mother!

MOTHER: (*Off mike*) I'm coming. (*Fade in*) Is anything wrong, Jack? Oh! What in the world is that?

JACK: It's a beanstalk, Mother! The beans I got for the cow — you threw them out of the window — and they have taken root!

MOTHER: Why, the stems are as thick as young trees, and all twisted around each other, just like a ladder! I never saw such a queer sight!

JACK: It goes 'way, 'way up, into the clouds. I'm going to climb it, Mother, to see where it goes.

MOTHER: Oh, no, no, Jack! You mustn't do that! Who knows what might happen to you? You might get hurt.

JACK: I'm going to see where that beanstalk leads to. (*Fade*) Here I go, Mother!

MOTHER: Come back, Jack! Oh, come back!

MUSIC: (*Bridge*)

NARRATOR: Well, Jack climbed up, and up, and up, for hours, and at last he reached the top. He looked about him. There was not a tree nor a living person to be seen. Far away he saw what looked like a large castle. After he had rested a while, he started toward it. When he got there the sun was setting. (*Fade*) Jack knocked at the door.

SOUND: (*Knock on wood, door open*)

WOMAN: Who are you, boy?

JACK: My name is Jack. I just arrived here, after climbing and walking all day. Will you give me a bite to eat, please, and a place to sleep?

WOMAN: What! Don't you know my husband is a giant? He is away now, but he'll be back soon. He eats people. He'll eat you, if he finds you here. Go away now, lad.

JACK: Oh, please, kind woman! I have walked all day, and I'm so tired. Won't you let me in and hide me somewhere?

WOMAN: Well, you'll have to take a chance. Come along to the kitchen. It's right by the door. Here we are. Sit down at the table. And here's a piece of bread and some cheese for you.

SOUND: (*Rattle of dishes*)

JACK: (*Mouth full*) Thank you. You are very kind.

SOUND: (*Very loud knock on door*)

WOMAN: That's my husband, the giant! He will kill you, and me, too, if he finds you! Where can I hide you?

JACK: I'll crawl into the oven! Lucky for me there's no fire in it.

94

SOUND: (*Heavy footsteps*)

GIANT: (*Fade in*) Fe, fi, fo, fum! I smell the blood of an Englishman! I'll eat him! Where is he, wife?

WOMAN: There's nobody here, husband. A bird flew over the house with a piece of fresh meat in its beak this morning.

SOUND: (*Chairs moved about*)

GIANT: Well, I can't find anybody here, so perhaps you're right. Give me my supper now, wife.

MUSIC: (*Bridge*)

NARRATOR: The giant sat down to a supper of a whole roasted ox. After a while Jack quietly opened the door of the oven a crack and looked out.

When the giant finished eating, he roared to his wife to bring him his hen. It was a magic hen. Every time the giant said, "Lay!" it laid a golden egg.

Soon the giant grew tired of playing with his hen and fell asleep.

SOUND: (*Snores up and under*)

NARRATOR: (*Fade*) As soon as the giant was asleep, Jack crept quietly out of the oven.

JACK: (*Low*) Now's my chance! The giant is fast asleep! I'll take that hen and dash for the beanstalk.

SOUND: (*Low cluck of hen*)

MUSIC: (*Bridge*)

NARRATOR: Well, Jack's mother was very happy to see him, you may be sure, and she was very glad to have the hen that laid the golden eggs. Jack and his mother sold the golden eggs, and had enough money for all they needed.

But Jack kept thinking of the giant's castle, and longed to go there again. His mother begged him not to climb the beanstalk again, because the giant's wife would be sure to know him.

But early one morning, a few months later, Jack put on old clothes, and darkened his face and hands, and climbed the beanstalk a second time. He went right to the giant's castle. (*Fade*) The giant's wife came to the door when he knocked.

SOUND: (*Knock on door*)

WOMAN: What do you want, lad?

JACK: Please, kind woman, will you give me a bite to eat and a place to sleep?

WOMAN: No, I will not! My husband, the giant, would not like it.

JACK: Oh, please do!

WOMAN: Not long ago a boy came here, just as you do now. I let him in, and he ran off with the giant's magic hen.

JACK: Oh, but I am so tired and hungry!

96

WOMAN: Well, I really shouldn't let you in, but come along to the kitchen. Sit down here. And here's a bowl of soup for you.

SOUND: (*Rattle of dishes*)

JACK: Thank you. You are very kind.

SOUND: (*Loud knocking at door*)

WOMAN: That's my husband, the giant! Oh, dear! If he finds you here he will kill you, and me, too. What shall I do?

JACK: Hide me somewhere! Here! In this closet!

SOUND: (*Door shut, heavy footsteps*)

GIANT: (*Fade in*) Fe, fi, fo, fum! I smell the blood of an Englishman! Where is he, wife?

WOMAN: There's nobody here, husband. A bird flew over the roof with a piece of fresh meat in its beak.

GIANT: Let me search. I don't want anybody running off with another of my magic treasures.

SOUND: (*Chairs moved*)

WOMAN: I saw no man here to-day, husband.

97

GIANT: It was a boy the other time, you told me. Well, I can't find anybody, so bring me something to eat, wife. Ah, come here, my good little dog. Sit here by me while I eat. Good doggie!

SOUND: (*Bark of dog*)

MUSIC: (*Bridge*)

NARRATOR: The giant was soon eating a huge supper. When he had finished, he called to his wife to bring him a bag of gold pieces to play with. After a while he got tired of the gold. He put it back into the bag and fell fast asleep in his chair.

SOUND: (*Snores up and under*)

NARRATOR: (*Fade*) Jack crept quietly out of the closet.

JACK: (*Softly*) Now's my chance! I'll take that money and run for the beanstalk!

SOUND: (*Bark of dog, not too loud*)

JACK: Here, doggie! Take this bone and be quiet.

MUSIC: (*Bridge*)

98

NARRATOR: It was a good thing for Jack that he found the bone on the giant's plate, so that the dog stopped barking and did not waken the giant. Jack made his way safely down the beanstalk. His mother was very happy to see him, and happy to have all that money, too. For three years all went well with Jack and his mother. But Jack kept thinking about the giant and the castle at the top of the beanstalk. At last he could stand it no longer. His looks had changed after three years, and early one morning he changed them still more by darkening his face and hands. Then he climbed the beanstalk without telling his mother. The giant's wife did not know him, (*Fade*) but still he had a hard time making her let him in.

WOMAN: My husband, the giant, still remembers the boy who ran off with his gold. Well, you do look very tired, young man, so I'll take a chance. Come with me to the kitchen.

JACK: Thank you very much, kind woman.

WOMAN: Here, sit down at this table and eat.

SOUND: (*Rattle of dishes*)

JACK: Thank you. This tastes very good.

SOUND: (*Loud knock at door*)

WOMAN: Oh, dear! Oh, dear! That's my husband, the giant! What ever shall I do with you? He'll kill us both if he finds you.

JACK: You must hide me somewhere! I can't get into the oven because there's a fire in the stove. Here! I'll get inside this big soup kettle. Put the cover on, quickly!

SOUND: (*Metal cover on pot*)

GIANT: (*Fade in*) Fe, fi, fo, fum! I smell the blood of an Englishman! Be he alive, or be he dead, I'll grind his bones to make my bread! Where is he, wife?

WOMAN: There's nobody here, husband. A bird flew over the roof with a piece of meat in its mouth.

GIANT: That's what you told me the other times, when those boys ran off with my hen and my gold. Let me look.

SOUND: (*Banging noises*)

GIANT: No one under the table. No one in the store room. No one behind the door. These big pots and kettles? They are all covered, so no one could be in one of them. Well, I can't find anybody, but I'm sorry for him if I do!

WOMAN: Do sit down and eat your supper, husband. You must be hungry.

GIANT: Yes, I am hungry.

SOUND: (*Rattle of dishes*)

GIANT: This ox is very good, wife. You are a good cook.

WOMAN: I thought you might like your magic harp to play to you while you eat, so I put it on the table for you.

GIANT: A good idea. This magic harp plays sweet music. Play, harp, play sweet music for me.

MUSIC: (*String music softly*)

NARRATOR: The harp played softly while the giant ate. The big meal and the music made the giant sleepy, and soon he was fast asleep.

SOUND: (*Snores up and under*)

NARRATOR: Jack had lifted the top of the kettle a bit when the harp started playing. (*Fade*) Now he softly stepped out of the kettle and went to the table.

JACK: (*Low*) Ah! Now's my chance to take the harp and run for the beanstalk!

VOICE: (*Soft and sweet, as of harp*) Master! Wake up, Master! Wake up, Master!

SOUND: (*Snores out*)

GIANT: Ha! What's this? The voice of my magic harp! Somebody has run off with it! I must go after him! Stop, thief! Give me back my harp! Stop! Stop!

JACK: (*Off mike*) Catch me if you can!

SOUND: (*Running steps, harp music*)

JACK: Mother! Mother! Oh! I'm so glad I got down to our garden! Mother! The giant is after me! Bring me an axe, quick! I must chop down the beanstalk! Oh, be quick, Mother!

MOTHER: Here's the axe, Jack, darling!

SOUND: (*Axe chopping*)

MOTHER: Oh, I can see the giant starting down the top of the beanstalk! Chop harder, Jack, harder! The beanstalk is falling!

SOUND: (*Crash of wood, heavy falling body*)

JACK: Ah! There's the giant, on the ground! He's still now. His fall from the beanstalk has killed him, Mother.

MOTHER: Lucky for both of us, my son.

JACK: Lucky for everybody, Mother. Now he'll never kill anybody again.

MOTHER: Oh, Jack! I'm so glad the beanstalk is down. Now I won't have to worry about your climbing it.

JACK: I'll never have to climb it again, Mother. With the hen that lays golden eggs, the giant's gold, and the magic harp, we have all that we need to keep us in comfort for the rest of our lives.

MUSIC: (*Up and out*)

ANNOUNCER: And so ends *Jack and the Beanstalk*, our story from England. I'm sure Jack's mother was glad when the beanstalk was cut down. Then Jack could not get into danger by climbing it.

Listen to our next tale which comes from Japan. It is called *Shiro and His Master*.

hiro and

CAST   Moto   King
          Wife   Announcer
          Saki   Narrator

SOUNDS

Crack of whip

Wind blowing

Shovel

Dog barking — whining

Clink of money

His Master

ANNOUNCER: Hello, boys and girls! It's story time. Today we will tell you a story that comes from Japan. The name of this story is *Shiro and His Master*.

MUSIC: (*Up and out*)

NARRATOR: There once lived in Japan an old man and his old wife. Their children had grown up and married, and the old man and his wife were very lonely. So they took in a homeless dog that they found wandering in the streets. They named him Shiro and were very kind to him. One day the old man, whose name was Moto, (*Fade*) heard the dog barking in the garden.

SOUND: (*Dog bark off mike*)

MOTO: That's Shiro barking. What do you suppose he is barking at, wife?

WIFE: Perhaps he's only barking at the crows to keep them out of our garden.

MOTO: I wouldn't want him to frighten any passing stranger. (*Fade*) I'd better go and see.

SOUND: (*Barking up and under*)

MOTO: What is it, Shiro? Why are you barking so? And what are you digging for under that old dead tree? Did you bury a bone there?

SOUND: (*Bark out*)

MOTO: Oh! Oh! Wife! Come out here, quickly!

WIFE: (*Off mike*) What's the trouble, husband?

MOTO: Come out here, and bring a shovel and a large basket. Good Shiro! Good dog! You shall have an extra bone.

WIFE: (*Fade in*) Here's the shovel and the basket. What do you want them for?

MOTO: Look, wife! Gold! Shiro has dug up all these gold pieces from under the dead cherry tree.

WIFE: Oh, how wonderful! Shovel them into the basket.

SOUND: (*Clink of gold pieces*)

WIFE: Now we shall have enough money for all our needs. Good Shiro! Good doggie!

SOUND: (*Bark*)

MUSIC: (*Bridge*)

NARRATOR: As you can imagine, the old man and his wife were very happy to have all this gold. They told the story of Shiro and praised him to everybody in the village. Now there was one neighbor, a man named Saki, who had never liked Shiro and had always thrown stones at the dog. But when Saki heard the story of the gold, (*Fade*) he went to Shiro's master and said,

SAKI: Good morning, Moto.

MOTO: Good morning, neighbor Saki.

SAKI: Moto, will you lend me your good dog for a while?

MOTO: You want to borrow Shiro?

SAKI: Yes, please, just for a few days.

MOTO: But you are always throwing things at him, and now you are calling him a good dog.

SAKI: Oh, no! I never throw things at him. It's only that he gets in the way when I am clearing my garden of sticks and stones.

MOTO: But what do you want Shiro for?

SAKI: Well, somebody is stealing my vegetables, and I want the dog to help me catch the thief.

MOTO: In that case, you may borrow Shiro if he can be of use to you. Shiro! Shiro! Go with our neighbor. Go, I said!

SOUND: (*Bark*)

MOTO: You'll be back soon.

SOUND: (*Fade bark*)

MUSIC: (*Bridge*)

NARRATOR: So Saki took Shiro to his own garden where there was a cherry tree just like Moto's tree. (*Fade*) He pressed the poor dog's nose hard against the earth under the tree.

SAKI: (*Crossly*) Dig, Shiro, dig!

SOUND: (*Whine of dog*)

SAKI: Dig up gold for me. Dig, I say! I want gold, like the gold you dug up for your master. Nothing but mud you find for me. If you don't find gold, I'll beat you! You are a lazy, good-for-nothing animal!

SOUND: (*Crack of whip, dog's whine fading*)

SAKI: That's the end of you, you good-for-nothing dog! I'll bury you right here, in the hole under the tree where you would not find gold for me.

MUSIC: (*Bridge*)

NARRATOR: The next morning old Moto went to his neighbor's house to ask about Shiro.

MOTO: Good morning, Saki. Are you ready to return my dog Shiro? My wife and I are lonesome without him.

SAKI: No, I can't.

MOTO: You still need him?

SAKI: No. If you must know, I have killed Shiro.

MOTO: What! Killed Shiro? But why?

SAKI: Oh, he did a great deal of harm around here. Instead of watching my vegetables, he dug them up.

MOTO: I can hardly believe Shiro would do such a thing. He was always a good dog. Oh, dear! What will my wife say? She was so fond of him.

SAKI: That's all I have to say, Moto. I have work to do.

MOTO: Well, since I can't have Shiro, will you please give me some wood of the tree under which my poor dog is buried?

SAKI: Yes, that I'll do. The tree is no good to me. You may have it if you chop it down yourself.

MOTO: Thank you Saki.   I'll make a mixing bowl for my wife out of the wood.   I'll go get my axe.

MUSIC: (*Bridge*)

NARRATOR: So old Moto made a mixing bowl out of a piece of the tree under which Shiro was buried.   Now a strange thing happened.   Just as soon as Moto's wife put a handful of flour into the bowl, it was changed at once into a bowlful of sweet cakes.   Some of these cakes were put on the grave of the dead dog, but there were enough left over for a feast for the neighbors. When the bad neighbor, Saki, heard the story of the wonderful bowl, of course he wanted it for himself. (*Fade*) So he said to Shiro's master,

SAKI: You were very kind to ask me to the feast, Moto.

MOTO: You were very welcome, Saki.

SAKI: I'm very sorry I killed Shiro, so I, too, would like to put some cakes on his grave.

MOTO: That would be right for you to do.

SAKI: Well then, Moto, will you lend me your mixing bowl?

MOTO: Well — it's not a large bowl, Saki.

SAKI: I know. But I want just a few cakes, and it is right that they should be mixed in this bowl made from the tree under which Shiro is buried.

MOTO: Well — take it. But please be careful of my bowl, Saki.

SAKI: Oh, I'll be careful of it. I'll return it soon. Thank you, and goodbye.

MUSIC: (*Bridge*)

NARRATOR: As soon as Saki got back to his own house, he put some flour into the bowl and waited for the flour to turn into a pile of sweet cakes. But the flour changed into black mud that splashed all over Saki. He was so angry that he threw the bowl full of mud into a corner of his garden, and set fire to the bowl. (*Fade*) The next day old Moto came to ask for his bowl.

MOTO: Good morning, neighbor Saki. I've come to take my mixing bowl back. That is, if you have no more use for it.

SAKI: Your mixing bowl? Oh, I burned it, if you must know.

MOTO: You burned my wonderful bowl?

SAKI: What was so wonderful about it?

MOTO: Why, when my wife put only a handful of flour into it, there were dozens of sweet cakes for us, ready baked.

SAKI: It did nothing of the sort for me. My flour changed into black mud, so I threw it all out and burned the bowl.

MOTO: My wonderful bowl! My wife and I liked it so, because it was made of the tree under which poor Shiro is buried.

SAKI: Well, there's no use crying over it, Moto. It's nothing but ashes now.

MOTO: Well then, will you let me take the ashes, please?

SAKI: What do you want with the ashes?

MOTO: They'll make me think of my good dog Shiro.

SAKI: Take the ashes. You'll be helping to clear my garden.

MOTO: Thank you, neighbor Saki. I'll go get a basket to carry the ashes in.

MUSIC: (*Bridge*)

NARRATOR: So old Moto sadly took up the ashes of the burned bowl. His wife was weeding their garden. When he told her what the ashes were, she felt just as sad as he did. (*Fade*) She asked,

WIFE: But what do you mean to do with the ashes, husband?

MOTO: They're all I have to make me think of poor Shiro. I'll bury them in the hole under the cherry tree, where he dug up the pieces of gold for us.

WIFE: Well, the ashes can't harm the tree. It's all dried up, and hasn't blossomed for many years.

MOTO: I'll put them into the hole and cover them with earth, carefully, so.

SOUND: (*Shovel digging*)

WIFE: It's a pity about this tree. It used to have such beautiful pink blossoms, like clouds at sunset.

MOTO: Yes, it is a pity that it died. Why — why, look, wife!

WIFE: Oh! How strange! The tree is putting out green leaves! They're growing as we watch!

III

MOTO: And look! Tiny flowers —
no, they're growing! Blossoms!
The tree is in full bloom!

WIFE: It's wonderful! It's magic!

MOTO: It must be because of the ashes, wife.
There must be magic in those ashes.
Come, let's run and tell our neighbors!
(*Fade*) Let's call our neighbors to see this tree!

MUSIC: (*Bridge*)

NARRATOR: By and by the whole countryside learned of
the magic ashes that had made a dead tree blossom.
Even the King in his palace heard the story. He sent
a messenger to bring Moto and some of the magic
ashes to the palace. (*Fade*) The King met the old man
in the palace garden.

KING: So you are Moto, the man who makes trees blossom.

MOTO: Your servant bows low before you, your Majesty.

KING: And have you brought some of your magic ashes,
old man?

MOTO: I have, your Majesty, here in this basket.

KING: Good! Now, this cherry tree used to be the finest
tree in my garden. It had the loveliest pink blossoms
in the country.

MOTO: It is still a young tree, your Majesty, and should
be flowering.

KING: I know, but none of my gardeners can make it
bloom again. That's why I sent for you. See if your
ashes can do as much magic in my garden as they did
in your own.

MOTO: I shall be glad to try, your Majesty. I'll take a pinch of the ashes between my fingers — so — and throw them up at this lower branch. Let's watch, your Majesty.

KING: By all the gods! Tiny green leaves are coming out on the bare twigs! They're growing bigger! Leaves, green leaves are growing!

MOTO: And see, your Majesty! Little pink buds, ready to open!

KING: The buds are opening as I watch. The whole branch is flowering! Wonderful!

MOTO: And now, your Majesty, I'll take a whole handful of these magic ashes and throw them carefully up into the tree so the breeze will carry them to every branch. There!

KING: Ah! The whole tree has burst into bloom! It is just as it used to be every Spring, covered with sweet-smelling pink blossoms. How happy I am to see it so again!

MOTO: I am glad I was able to make the tree bloom again, your Majesty.

KING: You must be a very good man, Moto, if you can work such wonders.

MOTO: It is not I who have done this, but the spirit of my good dog Shiro, which must be in these ashes.

KING: But you must have been very good to the dog if his spirit works magic for you even when he's dead. Come into my palace, Moto, and I shall pay you much gold for what you have done for my favorite cherry tree. I shall also give you some presents for yourself and your good wife.

MOTO: Thank you, your Majesty!   You are very kind.

MUSIC: (*Bridge*)

NARRATOR: So old Moto went home with gold and many gifts from the King.   When his neighbor, Saki, heard of Moto's good fortune, he was more jealous and angry than ever.   He made up his mind that he, too, would go to the King's palace and get some gold for himself. So he took a large basket of ashes from his fireplace, (*Fade*) and he stood at the gate to the palace garden, crying,

SAKI: I am the man who can make trees blossom!   I am the man who can make trees blossom!   Who wants his trees to blossom?

KING: Old man out there!

SAKI: Yes, your Majesty?

KING: Come into my garden.   The gate is open.

SAKI.   Thank you, your Majesty.

KING: Can you really make trees bloom?

SAKI: I have some magic ashes in my basket, your Majesty, to make trees blossom.

KING: This tree by the gate is not blooming as it should. See what you can do for it.

SAKI: It is a very hard trick of magic, your Majesty, and I shall have to ask much gold for doing it.

KING: The King does not bargain, old man!   You shall have the gold if you do the work.

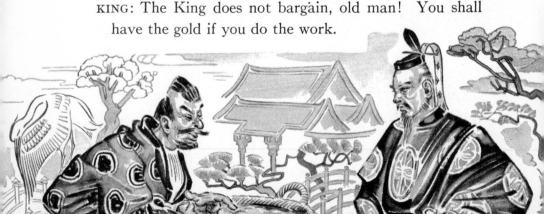

SAKI: Very well. Now, I take some of these ashes out of my basket, and throw them up at the branches of the tree, so.

KING: But nothing is happening, old man. The branch is still brown and dead.

SAKI: I'll throw some more ashes at the tree, your Majesty.

KING: The tree is still dead. You have not told the truth, old man. Your ashes are not magic ashes, like Moto's.

SAKI: Wait! I'll throw the rest of the ashes up into the tree. That will surely make it bloom, your Majesty.

SOUND: (*Wind blowing*)

KING: Here! What are you doing, old man? Your dirty ashes are flying all over me, and into my mouth, and my eyes! You cannot do the magic trick you promised. You don't know how to make trees blossom! Take this man away, soldiers, and throw him into prison for telling a lie and trying to fool the King. Away with him!

MUSIC: (*Bridge*)

NARRATOR: So the mean neighbor, Saki, was thrown into prison and kept there for many years. But the good Moto and his wife lived happily on the gold that the dog Shiro had found for his master and the gold that the King had given them.

MUSIC: (*Up and out*)

ANNOUNCER: And so ends the story of *Shiro and His Master*. We are glad that the good Moto and his wife had such good luck.

Be sure to listen to our next tale which comes from France. It is *The Sleeping Beauty*.

The Sleeping

CAST

KING   OLD WOMAN

QUEEN   PRINCE

THIRTEEN FAIRIES   JOHN

PRINCESS   ANNOUNCER

NARRATOR

SOUNDS

Dogs barking
Roosters crowing

Tapping of cane

Pounding of cane

Sound of bell

Door open

Beauty

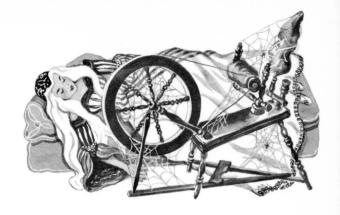

ANNOUNCER: It is time again for one of our *Tales from the Four Winds*. Today you will hear a story that children have asked for over and over again. The name of the story is *The Sleeping Beauty*.

MUSIC: (*Up and out*)

NARRATOR: Once upon a time there lived a king and a queen, who didn't have any children for a long time. At last a baby girl was born to them. The King and Queen were very happy, and so were all their people. The church bells rang all day, and everybody made merry. (*Fade*) The King and Queen planned a grand party at the palace.

KING: We must invite all the great people of the kingdom to this party, my dear, all the nearby kings, and queens, and princes, and princesses.

QUEEN: Especially the young princes.

KING: Why especially the young princes?

QUEEN: What a question, my dear husband! Our little daughter is a princess, and she must marry a prince, the handsomest prince in all the world.

KING: (*Laughs*) Our little daughter is only a few days old, and you are already worrying about a husband for her!

QUEEN: Well, it's never too soon, for a princess. Oh! I almost forgot! It would never do to forget *them!*

KING: Forget whom, my dear?

QUEEN: The little people, the fairies that watch over babies.

KING: Oh, of course! We must invite them.

QUEEN: Our little princess would never have any good luck if we forgot to ask them.

KING: But how do we go about it?

QUEEN: Why, don't you remember?

KING: I'm afraid not, my dear.

QUEEN: The way to do it is to write our invitation and tie it to the stem of a bluebell in the garden. The fairies love to swing in bluebells, and so they'll be sure to see our invitation.

KING: How many of these fairies are there in our kingdom?

QUEEN: Twelve, my dear.

KING: Only twelve?

QUEEN: Well, there used to be thirteen, but the thirteenth hasn't been seen or heard from in so many years that everybody believes she has gone somewhere else to live. I'm really glad of that.

KING: Glad? Why?

QUEEN: Because, you see, we have only twelve extra-fine gold plates good enough for these fairies.

KING: Oh, I see. Well, our princess will have a fine party!

QUEEN: And beautiful gifts from the fairies, I'm sure. I wonder what they'll give her.

MUSIC: (*Bridge*)

NARRATOR: Yes, it was a grand party. All the fairies came, and all the kings, and queens, and princes, and princesses came, too, and each brought a gift for the baby princess. When it was the turn of the fairies to give their gifts, (*Fade*) each fairy waved her magic wand as she spoke.

SOUND: (*Sound of tiny bell before each fairy's wish*)

FIRST FAIRY: The Princess shall grow more and more beautiful each day.

SECOND FAIRY: The Princess shall be so good that everyone shall love her.

THIRD FAIRY: The Princess shall sing like a bird.

FOURTH FAIRY: The Princess shall be kind, and never say a mean word.

FIFTH FAIRY: The Princess shall always have much gold.

SIXTH FAIRY: The Princess shall be as happy as the day is long.

SEVENTH FAIRY: The Princess shall dance as lightly as a leaf on a tree.

EIGHTH FAIRY: The Princess shall always speak the truth, and never an ugly lie shall pass her lips.

NINTH FAIRY: The Princess shall never know a day of sickness.

TENTH FAIRY: The Princess shall be clever and wise.

ELEVENTH FAIRY: The Princess shall be fair and just.

TWELFTH FAIRY: The Princess shall be —

SOUND: (*Pounding of cane*)

THIRTEENTH FAIRY: What's this? What's the meaning of this? Why wasn't *I* invited?

VOICES: The thirteenth fairy! The old fairy! She hasn't been seen for years! The thirteenth fairy!

THIRTEENTH FAIRY: Why wasn't *I* invited, I ask? Such a mean trick!

QUEEN: (*Frightened*) If you please, kind fairy —

THIRTEENTH FAIRY: I'm not a kind fairy! I'm a very angry fairy!

QUEEN: But — but — nobody has seen you here for such a long, long time that we all thought you had gone somewhere else to live.

THIRTEENTH FAIRY: A poor excuse! No excuse at all! Now I shall give the baby princess *my* gift.

QUEEN: Oh, please be as kind as your sister fairies have been!

THIRTEENTH FAIRY: Quiet! The Princess may keep all the gifts my sisters have given her. I cannot take them away. But when she is fifteen years old, she shall prick her finger while spinning and fall down dead!

VOICES: Oh! How terrible! The poor child! Oh!

THIRTEENTH FAIRY: Now I go!

SOUND: (*Tapping of cane fading*)

QUEEN: (*Weeps*) My little baby! Fairies, speak! Can't you take away the cruel wish of the old fairy?

TWELFTH FAIRY: Do not weep so, good Queen. I, the twelfth fairy, had not yet given my wish to the baby when my older sister fairy came in.

QUEEN: Then surely you can take away the wicked wish!

TWELFTH FAIRY: I cannot do away with it entirely, but I can soften it.

QUEEN: Oh, please, please change that wicked wish!

TWELFTH FAIRY: Here is my gift. When the Princess is fifteen, she shall indeed prick her finger with a spindle —

VOICES: Oh! Oh! Oh!

TWELFTH FAIRY: But she shall not die. Instead, she shall fall into a deep sleep. She shall sleep for a hundred years, and then she shall be awakened, but only by a prince.

QUEEN: Oh, kind fairy! Thank you! Thank you a thousand times!

VOICES: The Princess shall not die! The Princess shall not die!

KING: I, the King of this land, order that every spinning wheel and every spindle in the kingdom shall be burned, at once! There shall not be one spindle left in the whole land!

VOICES: All the spinning wheels and spindles shall be burned!

KING: And now, my friends, let us go on with our merry-making. Musicians, a gay dance!

MUSIC: (*Old dance*)

NARRATOR: As she grew up, the little Princess showed that she had all the gifts of the fairies. Her parents loved her so much that they hardly ever let her out of their sight. On the morning of her fifteenth birthday, however, it happened that she was alone. The servants were busy getting ready for her birthday party, and the King and Queen were sitting on their thrones, listening to people who came to beg for favors. So the Princess wandered from room to room in the large castle. By and by she came to an old tower with a winding stairway. She climbed and climbed up the dusty steps. At last she came to the top. There she found a little door. In the lock was an old key. She turned the key and the door opened.

SOUND: (*Door open*)

PRINCESS: What a queer room!

WOMAN: Come in, little girl.

PRINCESS: I am the Princess, old woman. Good day to you.

WOMAN: Good day to you, Princess. I am too old to rise and bow to you.

PRINCESS: Oh, you need not rise for me. What are you doing?

WOMAN: I am spinning.

PRINCESS: Spinning? What is that?

WOMAN: I take this wool and draw it out into fine threads.

PRINCESS: I see! You make the big wheel go round, and the thread goes on to this pointed stick. What do you call this stick?

WOMAN: That's a spindle, Princess.

PRINCESS: A spindle. It must be fun to make the wheel go round. Will you let me try to spin, old woman?

WOMAN: Certainly, Princess. Be sure the thread winds smoothly on the spindle.

PRINCESS: This *is* fun! Oh! My finger! (*Sleepy*) Oh! Oh!

MUSIC: (*Soft music*)

NARRATOR: As soon as the Princess touched the spindle the wish of the thirteenth fairy came true. She fell to the floor. But she was not dead, only fast asleep. Everybody and everything in the castle fell asleep. The King and Queen fell asleep on their thrones. The horses slept in the barns, the dogs stopped barking and went to sleep. The fire in the fireplace became still. The flies slept on the ceiling. The wind stopped blowing, and not a leaf stirred.

MUSIC: (*Soft music*)

NARRATOR: A tall, thick hedge of thorns sprang up around the castle, so that only the tops of the towers could be seen. Years went by, and people told their children and grandchildren about the Sleeping Beauty in the castle. At last a young prince came riding through that land with his servant. He saw the tall towers above the hedge, (*Fade*) and he asked his servant about them.

PRINCE: What are those towers, John?

JOHN: Those, your Highness, belong to the castle of the Sleeping Beauty.

PRINCE: Oh, I remember! My grandfather used to tell me the story of the Sleeping Princess, as his father told it to him.

JOHN: It all happened about a hundred years ago.

PRINCE: My grandfather said the Princess was very beautiful.

JOHN: And they say she was as good as she was beautiful.

PRINCE: I must try to break through this hedge of thorns and get into the castle!

JOHN: But, your Highness, many princes have tried before you, and they were all held fast by the thorns.

PRINCE: I will get through and free the Princess from the magic spell, or die trying!

JOHN: I cannot let you go alone, your Highness. You might be hurt. I'm going with you.

PRINCE: Come with me, then, John. But I shall go first and look for the Princess myself.

JOHN: Look at the hedge, your Highness! How strange!

PRINCE: Why, the thorns are turning into roses! The hedge is parting for us, and we can go through without a scratch.

JOHN: It must be, your Highness, that the hundred years are up now, and that you are the chosen prince.

PRINCE: I hope so! See, John! Every living thing in the courtyard is asleep. Let us step softly, so that nothing will waken before the Princess herself does.

JOHN: Yes, your Highness.

PRINCE: All the doors are open. There are the King and the Queen, asleep on their thrones.

JOHN: And all the other people asleep in their chairs, or standing before the King, as if still begging for favors.

PRINCE: And the soldiers, standing guard at the doors, asleep. Let's go on, John. I wonder where this queer little winding stairway leads.

JOHN: I have heard, Your Highness, that the Princess sleeps high in a tower room.

PRINCE: I'll climb up there, John. You stay down here.

JOHN: Very well, your Highness. But do be careful.

MUSIC: (*Bridge*)

SOUND: (*Footsteps, door open*)

PRINCE: (*Low*) The Princess! How beautiful she is! I must touch her cheek.

PRINCESS: (*Soft sigh*) Oh! Why! Where am I? What am I doing here?

PRINCE: You have been asleep, Princess, for a long, long time.

PRINCESS: How long?

PRINCE: You have slept for a hundred years.

PRINCESS: But where is the old woman who was up here, and her spinning wheel?

PRINCE: People say she was not really an old woman, but a bad fairy who put you to sleep by her wicked magic. You could be wakened only by a prince, when the time was up.

PRINCESS: And you are the handsome Prince Charming who was to waken me!

PRINCE: Princess, you are the most beautiful girl I have ever seen. Will you marry me?

PRINCESS: Yes, my Prince.

SOUND: (*Dogs barking, rooster crowing*)

PRINCE: Do you hear all those sounds, Princess?

PRINCESS: Yes. What does it mean? Is anything wrong?

PRINCE: It means everything is right, now. All living things that slept while you slept are waking now.

PRINCESS: My parents, the King and Queen! I want to see them! They must be so worried about me!

PRINCE: I, too, want to see them. I want to ask them to let you marry me.

PRINCESS: Let's go downstairs, quickly.

PRINCE: I want to send my servant home to tell my own parents about my good luck and to ask them to come here. Then you and I can be married as soon as possible. Come, Princess, let me help you down the stairs.

MUSIC: (*Wedding march briefly*)

NARRATOR: And so the Prince and the Sleeping Beauty were married and lived happily ever after.

MUSIC: (*Up and out*)

ANNOUNCER: And so ends *The Sleeping Beauty*, our tale from France. Now you can see why the children of France and other children all over the world like this tale of the beautiful princess, the wicked fairy, and the handsome prince.

Our next story comes from Brazil. It is called *The Rock in the Sea*.

The Rock in

CAST	FATHER	OLD WOMAN
	MIGUEL	KING
	SANCHO	PRINCESS
	JOSE	ANNOUNCER
	NARRATOR	

SOUNDS

Waves on shore

Footsteps

the Sea

ANNOUNCER: Our tale to-day comes from Brazil. It is called *The Rock in the Sea* and tells of a beautiful Princess who was hidden in a rock far out in the sea. Listen and hear how she was saved.

MUSIC: (*Up and out*)

NARRATOR: Once upon a time there lived in Brazil a poor man who had three sons, Miguel (Me-gayl'), Sancho, and Jose (Ho-say'). The father rented a little patch of farming land from a rich land owner. But this piece of land did not give them a good living. One day, when the three brothers came in from the fields, (*Fade*) Miguel, the oldest one, said to his father,

MIGUEL: Thank heaven it's dark now, and I can stop working. I'm so tired, Father!

FATHER: You are a hard worker, Miguel, my son, and you, too, Sancho and Jose.

SANCHO: Yes, we work from dawn to dark, and what do we get out of it? A piece of bread and a cup of tea.

FATHER: I know, Sancho. Perhaps some day we can rent a bigger piece of land and make more money.

MIGUEL: That day is very far off!

SANCHO: You're right, brother Miguel.

MIGUEL: It's no use waiting for that day, Father. I've made up my mind. I'm not staying here any longer. I'm leaving.

129

FATHER: Leaving, my son?

MIGUEL: Yes. I'm going to the city, to find a place at the King's palace.

SANCHO: The King's palace! That sounds wonderful! I'm going with you!

FATHER: You will both leave me? But I can't work our little farm alone.

MIGUEL: Our brother Jose will still be here.

FATHER: Jose? He is only seventeen.

MIGUEL: But he's tall and strong for his age. You'll have to do the best you can. I won't stay here another day.

SANCHO: Neither will I. Well, Miguel, we should start at dawn, so we'll need a good night's sleep. Good night, Father.

MUSIC: (*Bridge*)

NARRATOR: So the two older brothers went off to the city. They never sent any letters or any money back to their father. After a year, the father grew worried about them and sent Jose to look for his brothers.

Jose took a loaf of bread and started out. With his sharp knife he cut his way through the jungle till he came to the mountains that kept the cold winds from the King's palace. As he stood wondering which road to take, he saw an old woman. (*Fade*) He greeted her politely.

JOSE: Good day to you, old woman.

WOMAN: Good day to you, my lad.   Where are you going?

JOSE: I'm off to the city, to find my two brothers.   But I'm not sure of my way.

WOMAN: I can tell you that.   Take this road to the right. It leads to the sea.   Keep watching for the sea.

JOSE: Thank you, old woman.

WOMAN: But I warn you, lad, that when you find your brothers, your troubles will only begin.

JOSE: Why do you say that?

WOMAN: You'll find out in good time.   But I shall give you something to help you win out.   Here.   Take these.

JOSE: What's this?   A sponge that fits into the palm of my hand, and a stick not too long to go into my pocket. What shall I do with these?

WOMAN: When the time comes, you'll know how to use them.

JOSE: Thank you, old woman.   But why are you so kind to me?

WOMAN: I am a wise woman with magic powers.   I have watched you and your brothers, and I know what a good son you have been.   That is why I wish to help you. Now, remember.   Keep on the road to the sea.

JOSE: I'll remember.   Goodbye, old woman, and thank you kindly.

MUSIC: (*Bridge*)

NARRATOR: So Jose followed the road to the sea. Soon he came to the city where the King lived, near the shore. Jose went right to the King's palace, hoping to find his two brothers. Now Miguel and Sancho had good jobs at the palace and had bought themselves fine clothes. When they saw Jose enter the courtyard in his poor clothes, they made believe not to know him, (*Fade*) and went off to a corner to talk about him.

MIGUEL: What can Jose be doing here, Sancho?

SANCHO: He must want money from us, Miguel. Well, I won't give him any.

MIGUEL: Neither will I. Perhaps he's bringing a letter from our father, asking us to come back and work that poor farm.

SANCHO: *I'll* never go back! Will you, Miguel?

MIGUEL: What? Give up my fine clothes and a good job for a little farm? I should say not!

SANCHO: Well then, we must get Jose out of the way.

MIGUEL: But how?

SANCHO: I have it! Let's get him into trouble with the King, and then he'll be put into prison where he won't bother us.

MIGUEL: I know just how to do that. We'll tell the King that Jose wants to look for the lost Princess.

SANCHO: That *will* make the King angry! It's three years now since the Princess was carried off by the magician and hidden in the rock in the sea, and every time a man tries to find her and fails, the King gets very angry and has the man thrown into prison.

MIGUEL: Let's go and talk to Jose now. We'll talk kindly as if we mean to do him a favor.

SANCHO: Yes, and then we'll take him before the King. (*Loud*) Jose! Oh, Jose! Such a grand surprise to see you here!

MUSIC: (*Bridge*)

NARRATOR: The two brothers pretended to be very glad to see Jose. They told him they would take him to the King, who would give him a good job at the palace. On the way to the palace they told him about the Princess (*Fade*) and how anxious the King was to have her found.

SOUND: (*Footsteps under*)

MIGUEL: If you find her, Jose, no reward will be too great for you to ask.

JOSE: But, really, brothers, I wouldn't know how or where —

SANCHO: Sh! We're at the door of the throne room. There's the King, sitting on his golden throne. We must bow low.

SOUND: (*Footsteps out*)

KING: Come forward, young men. You are Miguel and Sancho, are you not?

MIGUEL: Your Majesty honors us by remembering our names.

KING: And who is this lad with you?

SANCHO: He is our young brother, Jose, just come from our father's land on the other side of the mountains.

KING: Hm! He is not dressed like the brother of such rich men as you two.

MIGUEL: Oh, Jose cares nothing for clothes, your Majesty. He thinks only of climbing mountains and swimming. He is a wonderful swimmer.

KING: (*Eagerly*) You are a great swimmer, Jose?

JOSE: Oh, your Majesty, I swim well enough in the little lake near our farm, but I am not really a wonderful swimmer.

SANCHO: Our brother Jose is a modest lad. He does not like to boast. He's a fine swimmer. That's why we have brought him before you.

KING: Does he think he can —? I hardly dare to hope —.

MIGUEL: Yes, Jose says he wishes to try to save your daughter, the Princess, from the rock in the sea.

JOSE: Your Majesty, I never heard of the Princess before I came here. But my brothers tell me I ought to try to save her and bring her back to you.

KING: There's something about the honest way you speak that I like, Jose.

JOSE: Thank you, your Majesty.

KING: And do you think you can save my daughter the Princess, who is hidden in a huge rock that stands far out in the sea?

JOSE: But, your Majesty, hasn't anybody ever tried to swim out there?

KING: The rock is so far out, that the strongest swimmers have never been able to reach it.

JOSE: But can't anybody get out there in a boat?

KING: No. There are sharp rocks sticking up in the sea around the rock in which the Princess is kept, and all boats are dashed to pieces.

MIGUEL: (*Quickly*) Oh, I'm sure our brother Jose can swim out, your Majesty.

KING: Well, I have hoped and lost hope so often that it makes me very angry whenever another man fails. It is the law now, Jose, that any man who tries and fails shall be thrown into prison.

JOSE: Prison! Oh!

KING: That's the law. Are you still willing to try, Jose?

JOSE: Well, I want to help you, your Majesty, but I certainly don't want to go to prison. Yes, I'll try it.

KING: Very well, then. Soldier, blow your trumpet and say that the King and all his court will go to the seashore to watch Jose swim to the rock in the sea.

MUSIC: (*Fanfare*)

HERALD: (*Fade*) Hear ye! Hear ye! The King and all his court —.

MUSIC: (*Bridge*)

NARRATOR: So the King, and Jose, and his two brothers, and everybody else in the palace walked down to the seashore. Two servants placed a high golden chair on the sand, and (*Begin fade*) the King seated himself while the others stood around him.

SOUND: (*Surf up and under*)

KING: How rough the waves are to-day! Look, Jose. Do you see that black rock far out over the waves?

JOSE: Yes, your Majesty. From here it looks like a long, dark box. It must really be much bigger than it seems.

135

KING: You can't change your mind now, Jose. You must jump into the sea and swim for it.

JOSE: No, your Majesty, I'm not changing my mind. But — now's the time I need help more than I ever did in my life. I'll take out the two gifts that were given to me by an old woman I met on the road. Ah!

KING: What's that, Jose? It looks like a sponge.

JOSE: It *is* a sponge, your Majesty.

KING: But what will you do with it?

JOSE: (*Thoughtful*) The old woman said, "You'll know what to do when the time comes." Now's the time. Ah! I *do* know!

KING: What are you doing down on your knees? Are you trying to mop the ocean dry with that sponge?

VOICES: The fool! Trying to wipe up the ocean! With a sponge! (*Laughter*)

JOSE: Look, your Majesty, how the sponge is growing larger and larger. Now it's large enough for me to sit on. (*Fade*) There! I'm off to the rock in the sea!

VOICES: He's off! He's rowing! Watch him!

MIGUEL: Look, Sancho! Jose is sitting on the sponge and sailing away!

SANCHO: It's like a boat, Miguel! Jose is rowing with his hands, as if he had oars! How fast he's moving!

KING: A boat made of a sponge! Such a boat can't be hurt by the sharp rocks.

MIGUEL: (*Sneer*) That remains to be seen, your Majesty.

KING: That young brother of yours must be a clever lad.

SANCHO: We never thought him clever, your Majesty.

KING: It sounds as if you and Miguel are not too fond of your young brother Jose. Oh, look, look! Jose has stopped rowing! He is climbing up the side of the rock!

VOICES: He's reached it! He's reached the rock! He's climbing up! He's on top of the rock!

KING: Oh! What has he done? The rock is breaking up! The pieces are falling into the sea! Jose is getting back on the sponge! But where's my daughter? She must have drowned in the sea with the pieces of rock! My daughter! Oh, my daughter!

MUSIC: (*Brief bridge*)

SOUND: (*Sound of waves up and under*)

NARRATOR: Yes, the King and all the others saw Jose start paddling back alone on his magic sponge. When Jose reached the shore again, the sponge at once became small enough to fit into his pocket. (*Fade*) The King was angry. He called out —

SOUND: (*Waves out*)

KING: Come here, Jose! The rock has broken up and fallen into the sea. What happened to my daughter? Why did you let her drown?

JOSE: Your daughter is not drowned, your Majesty.

KING: Not drowned? Didn't she fall into the sea?

JOSE: No, your Majesty.

137

KING: Then what happened to her? Tell me, quickly!

JOSE: When I got to the top of the rock, your Majesty, I could see no door or cave where the Princess might be hidden. Then I remembered this little wand that the old woman had given me.

KING: You broke up that big rock with this little stick?

JOSE: I touched the rock with the wand, and the top of the rock fell away. Inside the rock I could see the Princess, lying as if in a deep sleep. But even as I looked at her, a white veil was thrown around her.

KING: And then what happened?

JOSE: The Princess, inside the white veil, became smaller and smaller, until she was entirely closed inside a pearl the size of a bird's egg. I took the pearl quickly and put it into my pocket.

KING: A pearl! Oh, my lovely daughter! Give me the pearl. I shall have it set in a pin and wear it always.

JOSE: Wait, your Majesty. Let me touch the pearl with my wand, gently, so.

KING: The pearl has split in half! What is that little thing inside? It's growing larger — and larger — and larger! It's my daughter, my darling daughter, come back to me! Speak to me, my darling child!

PRINCESS: (*Wondering*) Oh, father! What am I doing here? I feel as if I am waking out of a long sleep.

KING: You were asleep, my dear child, and the time you slept was like a bad dream to me.

PRINCESS: But how did I get here?

KING: That is a long story which I'll tell you later. But you owe your life to this fine young man, Jose.

PRINCESS: How can I ever thank you enough, young man?

KING: I shall reward him with a fine place in the palace. Come, everybody. I shall give a great feast to-night in thankfulness for the return of the Princess and in honor of Jose, who saved her.

MUSIC: (*Bridge*)

NARRATOR: And so Jose went to live in the palace with the King and the Princess. The King sent for Jose's old father to come and live there, too. As for Miguel and Sancho, they were driven out of the city for trying to play a mean trick on their young brother. After a few years Jose married the Princess, and became King when her father died.

MUSIC: (*Up full and out*)

ANNOUNCER: And so ends *The Rock in the Sea*, our tale from Brazil. Weren't you glad to know that the Princess was rescued, and that Jose married her?

Our next story is about a family in the United States. It is called *The Peterkins Try to Become Wise*.

139

The Peterkins Try

CAST

MR. PETERKIN
MRS. PETERKIN
AGAMEMNON
SOLOMON JOHN
ELIZABETH ELIZA

THE TWO LITTLE BOYS
MRS. STONE
BOOKSELLER
POSTMASTER
ANNOUNCER

NARRATOR

SOUNDS

Key in lock

Footsteps on road

Footsteps on wooden floor

Door open
Door slammed

Knock at door

ANNOUNCER: Hello, boys and girls! It's story time again. Today we will tell you a story about an American family who were always getting into trouble. The name of this story is *The Peterkins Try to Become Wise.*

MUSIC: (*Up and out*)

NARRATOR: The Peterkin family lived at the edge of a small village near Boston. There were Mr. and Mrs. Peterkin, and the children. What were their names? Well, the oldest, almost a young man, was called Agamemnon. His mother sometimes called him 'Memnon, and I'm sure he wouldn't mind if you called him that, sometimes. Then there were Solomon John, and Elizabeth Eliza, and the two little boys. These two little boys looked and acted and talked so much alike that nobody ever called them by their names. They were just the two little boys to everybody.

Now, things often happened to upset the Peterkins, and they seldom could think what to do. At such times they used to go for help to the lady from Philadelphia, a lady who often came to visit in the Peterkins' village. One day, when the lady from Philadelphia had gone home, the Peterkins were sitting around the breakfast table, wondering what they would do without her. (*Fade*) Mrs. Peterkin was saying,

MRS. PETERKIN: I hope nothing happens to upset us, now that the lady from Philadelphia has gone home.

MR. PETERKIN: We would never know what to do without her help.

ELIZABETH ELIZA: Mother, do you remember the time when you put salt into your coffee instead of sugar?

MRS. PETERKIN: I certainly do remember, Elizabeth Eliza. I can still remember the first taste of salty coffee.

AGAMEMNON: I remember how I went to the drug store for something to take the salt taste out. The man put many things, one after the other, into the coffee, but he couldn't get it to taste right.

MRS. PETERKIN: Yes, Agamemnon, the man changed the coffee to many different colors, but he couldn't make it taste like coffee with cream and sugar.

SOLOMON JOHN: And it wasn't until we asked the lady from Philadelphia that at last you got a cup of coffee fit to drink, Mother.

MRS. PETERKIN: And what she told us to do was so easy, Solomon John, wasn't it?

LITTLE BOYS: She said, "Why don't you make a fresh cup of coffee?"

MR. PETERKIN: That's right, my little boys. Nobody in our family had thought of doing that.

ELIZABETH ELIZA: And do you remember, Father, the time when the men had placed my new piano with its back to the room and the keys facing the windows? I had to sit outside on the porch and play the piano through the window.

MR. PETERKIN: It was lovely for you in the summer, Elizabeth Eliza, when the weather was warm and it didn't get dark till late.

ELIZABETH ELIZA: But it was not at all pleasant, Father, when the weather grew colder.

MR. PETERKIN: And none of us thought of turning the piano around so that the keys faced inside the room until you asked the lady from Philadelphia what to do.

MRS. PETERKIN: I'm afraid, husband, that we are not a very wise family. If only we could be wise!

MR. PETERKIN: I have heard it said, my good wife, that people who think become wise. Let us all sit still for a while and try to think. (*Short pause*) Well, children, has anyone had a thought come into his head?

CHILDREN: (*Singly*) No. No. No. No.

MRS. PETERKIN: Neither have I, children.

SOLOMON JOHN: I have heard, Mother, that thoughts come from books. People who have a great many books are wise.

MR. PETERKIN: Well, suppose we count up how many books our family has. Agamemnon, you're the oldest. Have you any books?

143

AGAMEMNON: I have an arithmetic book, Father. It's almost new, because I never got to the hard numbers in the back of the book.

MR. PETERKIN: And you, Solomon John? Books were your idea.

SOLOMON JOHN: I have a reader I used in the fourth grade, Father.

MR. PETERKIN: And what about you, Elizabeth Eliza?

ELIZABETH ELIZA: I have a book of poems to speak at school parties.

MR. PETERKIN: Fine! Perhaps you will have a chance to say one of them at a party before you leave high school. And you, little boys?

LITTLE BOYS: We have a spelling book.

MR. PETERKIN: Good! It is wise to know how to spell.

MRS. PETERKIN: I have a book, too, children. It's a cook book.

MR. PETERKIN: Well, get ready to count, Agamemnon. We have an arithmetic book, a fourth grade reader, a book of poems, a spelling book, and a cook book. How many does that make, Agamemnon?

AGAMEMNON: That makes — er — five books, Father.

LITTLE BOYS: Hurray! We have five books!

MR. PETERKIN: Quiet, boys. That's not many books. What we should have is a library.

AGAMEMNON: That's the thing, Father! We want a library.

MRS. PETERKIN: Let's all sit and think, children, how we should get one. (*Short pause*) Agamemnon, have you a thought?

AGAMEMNON: I will make a library, Mother.

MRS. PETERKIN: How will you go about it, Agamemnon? The lady from Philadelphia isn't here, so we can't ask her.

AGAMEMNON: There are some boards in the barn, and I have a hammer and some nails, and there we have our library!

LITTLE BOYS: We have a library! Hurray!

ELIZABETH ELIZA: Quiet, little boys! That would make only the bookcase part of the library, Mother.

MRS. PETERKIN: What else would you want, Elizabeth Eliza?

ELIZABETH ELIZA: Why, there should be books in the bookcase.

MRS. PETERKIN: Dear me! Of course there should! Let's all sit and think again. (*Short pause*)

SOLOMON JOHN: I know! I will write a book myself!

LITTLE BOYS: Solomon John will write a book! Hurray!

MRS. PETERKIN: Oh, Solomon John, do you believe you can?

SOLOMON JOHN: Yes, Mother. But I'll need the help of everyone else in the family.

MRS. PETERKIN: Let's all go into the living room and help Solomon John write his book.

LITTLE BOYS: We're all going to write a book! Hurray!

MUSIC: (*Bridge*)

145

NARRATOR: So all the Peterkins went into the living room to help Solomon John write his book. (*Fade*) Solomon John looked around and asked,

SOLOMON JOHN: Where's the ink? I must have ink to write a book.

MRS. PETERKIN: Ink? Dear me! We have no ink, Solomon John. Won't a pencil do?

SOLOMON JOHN: No, Mother. Books should be written in ink, the lady from Philadelphia once told me.

MRS. PETERKIN: Then it must be so. Dear me!

ELIZABETH ELIZA: I have heard that oak galls mixed with vinegar make very good ink.

BOYS: What are oak galls, Elizabeth Eliza?

ELIZABETH ELIZA: Oak galls, little boys, are little things like balls that grow on the twigs and leaves of oak trees.

SOLOMON JOHN: Let's send the little boys to the woods to get some oak galls for my ink.

MR. PETERKIN: Why not all go to the woods to look for oak galls, children?

MRS. PETERKIN: That's a very good idea, husband. I'll pack a lunch, and we can make a picnic of it. I'll cook some hard-boiled eggs right away.

LITTLE BOYS: We'll put on our rubber boots. Hurray for the picnic!

MUSIC: (*Bridge*)

OAK GALLS

NARRATOR: Well, the Peterkins enjoyed their picnic, but they had a hard time finding any oak galls. When, late in the afternoon, the family started for home, the large picnic basket held just two small oak galls.

Then came the matter of the vinegar. Mrs. Peterkin had used the last of her vinegar the night before, so they thought they would all go to their nearest neighbor to borrow some. The little boys put on their rubber boots, and off they all went down the road to the neighbor's house.

SOUND: (*Knock at the door*)

MRS. STONE: (*Off mike*) Come in!

SOUND: (*Door open*)

MRS. PETERKIN: Good evening, Mrs. Stone.

MRS. STONE: Oh, good evening, Mrs. Peterkin. I see you've brought your whole family. Why don't you go round to the front door, and I'll let you into the living room, like real company?

MRS. PETERKIN: No, thank you. The kitchen door is where we should be just now. We are really not visiting. We came over to say that we wish we had some good vinegar.

MRS. STONE: Well, if you want some good vinegar, the thing to do is to set some cider down in the cellar. In about a year it will turn to very good vinegar.

MRS. PETERKIN: But we mean we need it this evening, right now, in fact. Can you lend us some?

MRS. STONE: Oh! Why didn't you say so? Just how much do you need?

MRS. PETERKIN: All we want is about half a cup. You see, we're going to make some ink.

MRS. STONE: Make some ink! My stars! I'll lend you some ink, if you wish.

MRS. PETERKIN: No, thank you, Mrs. Stone. We'd rather make it ourselves. It will be fresher that way.

MRS. STONE: Well! Here, I'll pour some for you. Why must the ink be fresh?

MRS. PETERKIN: You see, my son, Solomon John, is going to write a book with it.

MRS. STONE: Solomon John write a book! Well, my stars!

MRS. PETERKIN: Thanks very much for this vinegar, Mrs. Stone. We'll let you read the book after it's written. Come along, children.

MUSIC: (*Bridge*)

NARRATOR: So the Peterkins went home and stirred the two oak galls into the vinegar, and by nighttime the ink was ready. (*Fade*) Then Solomon John remembered something else.

SOLOMON JOHN: I need a pen to write with.

AGAMEMNON: You may use mine, Solomon John. It's on the table, by my arithmetic book.

SOLOMON JOHN: Yours is just a plain steel pen, Agamemnon. That won't do.

AGAMEMNON: Why not?

SOLOMON JOHN: Well, I have made up my mind that my book shall be a book of poems, and I've heard that poets always use pens made out of the wing feathers of a goose. They are called quill pens. The lady from Philadelphia told me. I must have a quill pen.

QUILL PEN

ELIZABETH ELIZA: That shouldn't be hard to get. Let's go out to the barnyard and get a wing feather from one of our geese. Then you will have a quill pen.

MRS. PETERKIN: It's quite dark now, children. Perhaps we had better wait till tomorrow morning.

ELIZABETH ELIZA: I think we had better do it now, Mother. I remember that my teacher once made me learn a little poem,

> "If a task is once begun,
> Never leave it till it's done."

MRS. PETERKIN: And you still remember it, Elizabeth Eliza! How bright you are! Perhaps you, too, should try to write a book.

MR. PETERKIN: Our daughter is right, wife. We should not stop now. Let's all go out to the barnyard to look for a goose quill.

MRS. PETERKIN: Very well. We had better take some lanterns to light our way.

LITTLE BOYS: We'll go put on our rubber boots. The ground may be wet.

MR. PETERKIN: I'll light the lanterns in the kitchen, and we'll go out through the kitchen door. I'll carry one lantern, and you, Agamemnon, carry the other. Then Solomon John's hands will be free to pull a feather from a goose, and the rest of you can help him. Ready, everybody?

CHILDREN: Ready, Father.

MUSIC: (*Bridge*)

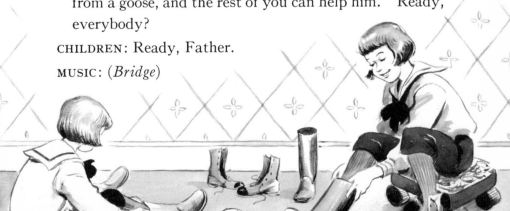

NARRATOR: And that's the way the Peterkins crossed the barnyard. Mr. Peterkin led the way with his lantern, Solomon John was behind him, Mrs. Peterkin and Elizabeth Eliza and the two little boys followed, and Agamemnon came last with his lantern.

The birds were sitting sleepily in their places, so that the Peterkins could look at each one carefully. But not a goose was to be found among them. There were hens, and roosters, and ducks, and turkeys, but not one goose, or even a goose feather. (*Fade*) As they started back across the yard to their house, Mrs. Peterkin said,

MRS. PETERKIN: I think we are the only geese on the place. Ha! Ha! Ha!

MR. PETERKIN: Children, your mother has just said something very funny. Ha! Ha! Ha!

CHILDREN: Mother has said something funny. Ha! Ha! Ha!

MUSIC: (*Bridge*)

NARRATOR: When the Peterkins were in the house again, (*Fade*) Solomon John sat down to think of the book of poems he wanted to write.

SOLOMON JOHN: Well, it's too bad we couldn't find a goose feather. What shall I do now?

AGAMEMNON: You're sure, Solomon John, that you won't use my steel pen, just this once?

SOLOMON JOHN: No, Agamemnon. All the pictures of the great poets of long ago show them writing with quill pens. How would it look if some one should walk in here and see me using a plain pen, such as any schoolboy might use?

ELIZABETH ELIZA: I remember seeing some quill pens in the bookstore on the road to the village.

MRS. PETERKIN: I don't know what we'd do if Elizabeth Eliza didn't sometimes remember things. Let's all go down to the bookstore and help Solomon John buy a quill pen.

LITTLE BOYS: We'll put on our rubber boots.

MRS. PETERKIN: No, boys. We haven't time to wait for that. It's very late, and the bookseller will be closing his store any minute. Let's hurry, everybody. Agamemnon, take the lantern to light the way.

MUSIC: (*Bridge*)

SOUND: (*Many footsteps on road, up and out*)

ELIZABETH ELIZA: Here's the bookstore now. Oh! The lights have just gone out. The man must be ready to lock up.

SOUND: (*Door shut loudly, key in lock*)

SOLOMON JOHN: Oh, Mr. Bookseller! Could you wait one minute, please?

BOOKSELLER: What is it, young man?

SOLOMON JOHN: We wanted to see your quill pens, if you please.

BOOKSELLER: Well, I was just going home, but I'll unlock the store to make a sale.

SOUND: (*Key in lock, door open*)

BOOKSELLER: I keep the quill pens on the table near the door. Lend me your lantern, please. I don't have much call for quill pens these days. How many do you people want?

SOLOMON JOHN: Oh, just one, sir. How much is it?

BOOKSELLER: You mean to say you all came for one quill pen and made me unlock the door for that? Ten cents, please. Good night, ladies and gentlemen!

SOUND: (*Door slammed, key in lock*)

SOLOMON JOHN: Good night, sir. My! He seemed a bit upset about something, didn't he?

MRS. PETERKIN: Well, you have your quill pen at last, Solomon John. Let's go home, so you can start your writing.

SOUND: (*Footsteps on road up and out*)

SOLOMON JOHN: Wait! I just remembered something else.

MRS. PETERKIN: What is it, Solomon John?

SOLOMON JOHN: I have a quill pen to write with now, but we have no paper at home to write on.

MRS. PETERKIN: Dear me! You must have paper to write the book on.

ELIZABETH: Why didn't you think of writing paper while the bookseller had his store open?

SOLOMON JOHN: You couldn't expect me to think of a pen, and paper, too, Elizabeth Eliza. And now the bookseller has gone home. Has anyone an idea what should be done?

MR. PETERKIN: Well, the post office is nearby. This is about the time when the last mail comes in. Perhaps there will be a letter for me. If there is, it may be a short one, written on only one side. Then you can use the other side for your book, Solomon John.

SOLOMON JOHN: But suppose it's a long letter, with writing on both sides, Father?

MR. PETERKIN: Well, in that case, you can use the back of the envelope to write on. We turn here for the post office.

MUSIC: (*Bridge*)

MR. PETERKIN: Here we are at the post office, everybody. The lights are on, which means that the postmaster is still in. Do you want to wait out here while I look into my mailbox, or would you all like to come inside with me?

ALL: We'll all go in with you.

SOUND: (*Door open, footsteps on wooden floor, up and out*)

MR. PETERKIN: Look, children! There's a letter in the Peterkin mailbox. It has come just at the right time.

LITTLE BOYS: Father has a letter! Hurray!

POSTMASTER: What's all the shouting about, Mr. Peterkin? Is this a very special letter you were expecting?

MR. PETERKIN: Oh, good evening, Mr. Postmaster. No, we weren't expecting a letter. We were just hoping we'd find one. You see, we need a sheet of paper to write on. My son, Solomon John, is planning to write a book, so that we can own a library and become a wise family, and so we need a sheet of paper for him to write the book on.

POSTMASTER: Well, is that so? In that case, Mr. Peterkin, I'll be glad to help out. I'll give your son a whole sheet of fresh, new paper that's never been written on. Here, Solomon John, take this big sheet of writing paper.

SOLOMON JOHN: Oh, thank you, sir! You are very kind.

POSTMASTER: Don't mention it. I'm glad to be of help to a writer of books. I hope you'll show me the book when it's finished.

SOLOMON JOHN: I certainly shall, Mr. Postmaster.

POSTMASTER: I must lock up now. Good night to all of you.

ALL: Good night, Mr. Postmaster.

MUSIC: (*Bridge*)

NARRATOR: When the Peterkins got home from the post office, they all sat down at the table to watch Solomon John start writing his book at last. Solomon John placed the paper before him, dipped the quill pen into the ink, and held it over the paper. The Peterkins all held their breaths. (*Fade*) Then Solomon John said,

SOLOMON JOHN: But what shall I write? I haven't anything to say. I haven't a thought in my head.

MRS. PETERKIN: Let's help Solomon John to think. Let's all try. (*Short pause*) Well, has anyone found a thought in his head?

ALL: No, we haven't a thought in our heads.

MRS. PETERKIN: Dear me! Then the Peterkins will never be wise!

MUSIC: (*Bridge*)

NARRATOR: And so, because neither Solomon John nor any other person in the Peterkin family could think of anything to write, Solomon John's book was never written. And the Peterkins never again tried to become a wise family.

MUSIC: (*Up and out*)

ANNOUNCER: And so, boys and girls, ends the story of the Peterkin family. We know that there are not many families who do such silly things, but it was fun to hear about the Peterkins.

This is the last of the *Tales from the Four Winds*. We hope that you have enjoyed all of them.

155

To the Teacher

OBJECTIVES

The use of the books in the series, *Tales from the Four Winds*, will achieve these worthwhile objectives: it will contribute to your pupils' literary background, will aid understanding of other peoples, and will provide a well-motivated and functional program in oral reading for both normal and remedial groups.

Building Literary Background

The stories in these books are mainly folk tales, some of them the familiar old favorites, others less familiar selections from the folk literature of various countries. Also included are some modern stories which have been so popular as to deserve a place in our children's literary background.

Faced with a crowded school program, the modern teacher understandably has difficulty finding the time and opportunity for the introduction of the old classics with which she feels her pupils should become familiar. In these books you will find such stories presented in a new and interesting form. They are written in a vocabulary which will be easily handled by the children for whom the books are intended.

Aiding Understanding of Other Peoples

The tales used in these books represent the folk lore of many different nations. By calling the children's attention to the fact that their favorite stories come from many lands, and by pointing out the similarities between stories from different countries, you will help to establish the understanding that people all over the world have many of the same basic interests, likes, and dislikes that we have. Emphasizing the likenesses between groups rather than their differences helps to form a feeling of fellowship for people of other lands.

Building an Oral Reading Program

In addition to contributing to literary background and to international good-feeling, these books supply an excellent source of supplementary oral reading material. The need for good teaching of oral reading is recognized by all educators. Dr. Paul McKee says, ". . . skillful teaching of oral reading is essential to the child's well balanced growth in the power to read."[1]

The tales in this series have been dramatized and are presented in the form of drama best known to modern children, the radio play. The dramatized form has a distinct advantage over the narrative form as material to be read orally, because it automatically creates the audience situation, without which oral reading becomes much less purposeful.

When a radio play is presented, the listener sees no costumes, no scenery, no facial expressions or gestures to help him grasp the spirit of the play and the meaning of the dialogue. His understanding and enjoyment of the play must depend completely on the clarity and expression with which the actors read their lines. Oral reading of this type of material, therefore, places a premium on correct pronunciation, clear enunciation, and good expression. Because a child reads the part of only one person in a radio play, he finds it easy to identify himself with that character and thus read the lines with adequate feeling. As most of the speeches are short, the young reader is much less self-conscious than he would be if he were reading a long prose selection for others.

The dramatic form is an excellent one for group activity. The fact that each person taking part must watch for

[1] McKee, Paul, *The Teaching of Reading.* Houghton Mifflin Co., Boston, 1948.

his own lines keeps each one alert and helps to maintain the interest of the entire group.

Through radio plays it is possible to use oral reading to entertain others. One group within the class may present a play for the rest of the class. Any one of the plays might be presented as a class project for other classes within the school. A radio play eliminates any necessity for costumes or scenery, as well as that of the actors' learning their lines verbatim. This type of program is especially good as a confidence builder for the shy, self-conscious child who dreads facing an audience.

These books will also prove useful in working with remedial groups. The short speeches are even more of an advantage in the remedial situation, because they help to relax the tension which many remedial readers feel when doing any oral reading at all. The short speech does not allow time for the tension to build up and become a block to performance.

The dramatic form simplifies the task of holding the attention of all members of the group, a task which is much more difficult with a remedial group than with a group of good readers. Using one of these plays, a remedial group might prepare a program for other children. The performance will give the members a sense of achievement in reading instead of the feeling of failure which they have experienced so frequently in the past.

Equipment

The simple sound effects suggested for these plays and the use of music between parts of the plays add to the interest by making the performances seem like the radio programs which children listen to and enjoy. While the plays may be read as a class activity without the sound effects or music, you will find that the added interest which sound effects and music bring to their performance is well worth the trouble of getting them ready beforehand. All the materials required for the sound effects are easily obtained, and the manipulation of the properties is never complicated. The children will enjoy experimenting in order to obtain the desired effect, and they may find substitutes for the materials suggested in the book. The music need not be elaborate. It may be supplied by a record player and records or by children singing or humming a part of a song which they already know.

To add to the illusion of a radio presentation, a make-believe radio studio may be constructed. A screen or curtain may be placed across one corner of the room in order to conceal the actors, a table and other properties for the sound man, and any musical equipment which is used. If you prefer, a screen which will rest on top of a table may be made by using cardboard from large cartons. A cloth hung from the edge of the table to the floor will conceal the actors' feet.

A make-believe microphone might be placed in the "studio." It can be made from an empty tin can, or from a chalk or cigar box painted silver. A hole should be made in the bottom of the microphone so that it will fit on a stand. For a stand you could use a discarded music stand or a broomstick set in a wooden base.

VOCABULARY

The objectives mentioned above are made easy of achievement because of the limited vocabulary used in the books. In *The Straw Ox and Other Tales*, the total number of different words, exclusive of proper names, is 1272, which is about two-thirds of the number of different words in some of the most widely used basic third readers. Of these 1272 words, ninety-five per cent are within a third grade reading vocabulary, as checked with *Stone's Graded Vocabulary for Primary Reading* and the Thorndike-Lorge *Teacher's Word List of 30,000 Words*.

Acknowledgments

The author wishes to make grateful acknowledgment to James F. Macandrew, Coordinator of Broadcasting for the Board of Education of the City of New York, for his encouragement and enthusiasm, for reading the section on production, and for contributing the directions for building a make-believe microphone.

Thanks are also offered to Dorothy Klock of the production staff of WNYE, whose imaginative production of many of these scripts has taught the author much about the possibilities of educational radio for younger children.

The author is deeply indebted to her sisters, Celia and Jeanne, whose unfailing thoughtfulness made possible the leisure to write these scripts.

Illustrators

Rumpelstiltskin, Shiro and His Master, and *The Rock in the Sea* were illustrated by Bruno Frost; *Boots and His Brothers* and *Lenka's Little House* by Robert Doremus; *The Three Wishes* and *The Peterkins Try to Become Wise* by Anne Fleur; *The Straw Ox* and *What the Good Man Does Is Right* by Walter Knapp; *Jack and the Beanstalk* and *The Sleeping Beauty* by Violet Lamont.